Important Notice

THIS BOOK IS *NOT A RETAIL PRICE LIST*

Premium prices are the average amount dealers will pay for coins (according to condition) if required for their stock.

(See page 14)

Current *retail* valuations of all U.S. coins are listed in Whitman's A GUIDE BOOK OF UNITED STATES COINS by R. S. Yeoman, Western Publishing Company, Inc., Racine, Wisconsin ($2.50).

Whitman Coin Folders are described on page 128.

Brief guides to grading are placed before each major coin type in this book. For those readers who desire more detailed descriptions of all coin grades, we recommend A GUIDE TO THE GRADING OF UNITED STATES COINS, by Martin R. Brown and John W. Dunn, Western Publishing Company, Inc., Racine.

BLUE BOOK OF UNITED STATES COINS

1972
HANDBOOK
OF
UNITED STATES
COINS

With Premium List

TWENTY-NINTH EDITION

By R. S. YEOMAN

Containing mint records and prices paid by dealers for all U. S. coins. Information on collecting coins — how coins are produced—mints and mint marks—grading of coins—location of mint marks—preserving and cleaning coins—starting a collection—what to buy—history of mints and interesting descriptions of all U.S. copper, nickel, silver and gold coins. Fully illustrated. INDEX PAGE 127.

Copyright © MCMLXXI

WESTERN PUBLISHING COMPANY, INC.

WHITMAN COIN SUPPLY DIVISION
RACINE, WISCONSIN

WHITMAN is a registered trademark of Western Publishing Company, Inc.

Foreword

Each year since 1941 new revised editions of this Handbook have aided thousands of people who have coins to sell or are actively engaged in collecting United States coins. The popular coin folder method of collecting by date series has set in motion ever-changing premium values based on the supply and demand of each date and mint mark of any type coin, such as the Lincoln cent. This book has, over the years, kept up with average coin values through its panel of contributors. It serves, too, as a source of general numismatic information of importance and usefulness to all levels of interest in the hobby.

This volume offers a helping hand to the new collector; explains what he should collect and what he should discard; tells him how to appraise and care for his coins. The simplest explanations are employed here, so that the reader may easily derive the utmost in enjoyment and profit from a collection of even the most common coins taken from ordinary pocket change.

While the primary purpose of this volume is to smooth the path toward numismatics for the beginner, much of the information, such as mint records, premium prices, varieties, and the like, will prove an invaluable aid to the more advanced collector.

The premium list gives representative prices paid by dealers for various United States coins. These prices have been assembled from many widely separated sources and are averages. Slight differences in prices among dealers on some issues depend on proximity to the various mints and populous centers. Other factors, such as local supply and demand, may also tend to raise or lower prices from those listed in this book. Many coins bring premium prices when uncirculated or proof, though they bring no premium when circulated.

CONTRIBUTORS

Lee F. Hewitt, the former editor and publisher of the NUMISMATIC SCRAPBOOK MAGAZINE, was an early contributor, having supplied many of the historical references and explanations which appear throughout this book.

The late Charles E. Green gave valuable counsel when the first edition of the HANDBOOK was undertaken. He supplied most of the mint data and was a regular contributor to each revised edition until his untimely death in late 1955.

CONTRIBUTORS TO THE TWENTY-NINTH EDITION

Kenneth E. Bressett — *Coordinating Editor*

A. E. Bebee
Philip E. Benedetti, Sr.
Q. David Bowers
Dan Brown
Malcolm O. E. Chell-Frost
Jerry Cohen
Carl Curcio
B. M. Douglas
Ben Dreiske
Kurt Eckstein
Pete Foerster
Charles E. French
Dorothy Gershenson
Bernard Gimelson

Ira M. Goldberg
Joseph Goldberg
Floyd O. Janney
Arthur Kagin
Paul Kagin
M. L. Kaplan
Mike Kliman
Abner Kreisberg
Gene Majors
Lester Merkin
Bill Mertes
Roy A. Miller
Ken Nichols
Dean Oakes

Al C. Overton
Joe Person
Elmer B. Ray
James F. Ruddy
Dick Rudolf
Earl C. Schill
Neil Shafer
Norman Shultz
Sidney W. Smith
Leonard Stark
Maurice A. Storck
Holland Wallace
Bob White
Gary Young

IF YOU HAVE COINS TO SELL

The publishers are not engaged in the rare coin business; however, the chances are that the dealer from whom you purchased this book is engaged in the buying and selling of rare coins — contact him first. In the event that you purchased this book from a source other than a numismatic establishment, consult your local telephone directory for the names of coin dealers (they will be found sometimes under the heading of "Stamp and Coin Dealers"). If you live in a city or town that does not have any coin dealers, it is suggested that you obtain a copy of one of the trade publications in order to obtain the names and addresses of many of the country's leading dealers.

Several popular magazines and papers are devoted to coin collecting:

COINage Magazine
16250 Ventura Boulevard
Encino, California   91316
(Monthly, single copy 60¢)

Numismatic Scrapbook Magazine
P.O. Box 150
Sidney, Ohio   45365
(Monthly, single copy 60¢)

Coins Magazine
Iola, Wisconsin   54945
(Monthly, single copy 60¢)

Numismatic News
Iola, Wisconsin   54945
(Weekly, single copy 25¢)

Coin World
P.O. Box 150
Sidney, Ohio   45365
(Weekly, single copy 35¢)

The Numismatist
P.O. Box 2366
Colorado Springs, Colo.   80901
(Published monthly by American
Numismatic Assn., single copy 75¢)

COLLECTING COINS

Numismatics or coin collecting is one of the world's oldest hobbies, dating back several centuries. Coin collecting in America did not develop to any extent until about 1840, as our pioneer forefathers were too busy carving a country out of wilderness to afford the luxury of a hobby. The discontinuance of the large-sized cent in 1857 caused many persons to attempt to accumulate a complete set of the pieces while they were still in circulation. One of the first groups of collectors to band together for the study of numismatics was the Numismatic and Antiquarian Society of Philadelphia, organized on January 1, 1858. Lack of an economical method to house a collection held the number of devotees of coin collecting to a few thousand until the Whitman Publishing Company and other manufacturers placed the low-priced coin boards and folders on the market some years ago. Since that time the number of Americans collecting coins has increased many-fold.

The Production of Coins

To collect coins intelligently it is necessary to have some knowledge of the manner in which our coins are produced. They are made in factories called "mints." The Mint of the United States was established at Philadelphia by a resolution of Congress dated April 2, 1792. The Act also provided for the coinage of gold eagles ($10), half-eagles and quarter-eagles, the silver dollar, half-dollar, quarter-dollar, dime (originally spelled "disme") and the half-disme or half-dime; the copper cent and half cent. According to the Treasury Department, the first coins struck were one-cent and half-cent pieces, in March of 1793 on a hand-operated press. Most numismatic authorities consider the half-disme of 1792 as the first United States coinage, quoting the words of George Washington as their authority, Washington, in his annual address, November 6, 1792, having said, "There has been a small beginning in the coining of the Half-Dimes, the want of small coins in circulation calling the first attention to them." In the new Philadelphia Mint are exhibited a number of implements, etc., from the original mint, and some coins discovered when the old building was wrecked. These coins included half-dismes, and the placard identifying them states that Washington furnished the silver and gave the coined pieces to his friends as souvenirs.

Prior to the adoption of the Constitution, the Continental Congress arranged for the issuance of copper coins under private contract. These are known as the "Fugio cents" from the design of the piece, which shows a sundial and the Latin word "fugio" — "I Fly" or, in connection with the sundial, "Time Flies." The ever appropriate motto, "Mind Your Business," is also on the coin.

In the manufacture of a given coin the first step is the cutting of the "die." Prior to the latter part of the nineteenth century dies for United States coins were "cut by hand." Briefly this method is as follows: The design having been determined, a drawing the exact size of the coin is made. A tracing is made from this drawing. A piece of steel is smoothed and coated with transfer wax, and the tracing impressed into the wax. The engraver then tools out the steel where the relief or raised effect is required. If the design is such that it can all be produced by cutting away steel, the die is hardened and ready for use. Some dies are not brought to a finished state, as some part of the design can perhaps be done better in relief. In that case, when all that can be accomplished to advantage in the die is completed, it is hardened, a soft-steel impression is taken from it, and the unfinished parts are then completed. This piece of steel is in turn hardened and, by a press, driven into another piece of soft-steel, thus making a die which, when hardened, is ready for the making of coins.

This hand method of cutting dies accounts for the many die varieties of early United States coins. Where the amount of coinage of a given year was large enough to wear out several dies, each new die placed in the coining press created another die variety of that year. The dies being cut by hand, no two were exactly alike in every detail. Of the cents dated 1794, over sixty different die varieties have been discovered.

Hundreds of dies are now used by the mints of the United States each year, but they are all made from one master die, which is produced in the following manner:

After the design is settled upon, the plaster of paris or wax model is prepared several times the actual size of the coin. When this model is finished an electrotype (an exact duplicate in metal) is made and prepared for the reducing lathe. The reducing lathe is a machine, working on the principle of the pantograph, only in this case the one point traces or follows the form of the model while another and much smaller point in the form of a drill cuts away the steel and produces a reduced size die of the model. The die is finished and details are sharpened or worked over by an engraver with chisel and graver. The master die is used to make duplicates in soft-steel which are then hardened and ready for the coining press. To harden dies, they are placed in cast-iron boxes packed with carbon to exclude the air, and when heated to a bright red are cooled suddenly with water.

In the coinage operations the first step is to prepare the metal. The alloys used are: silver coins, 90% silver and 10% copper; five-cent pieces, 75% copper and 25% nickel; one-cent pieces, 95% copper and 5% zinc. (The 1943 cent consists of steel coated with zinc; and the five-cent piece 1942-1945 contains 35% silver, 56% copper and 9% manganese.) Under the Coinage Act of 1965, the composition of dimes, quarters and half dollars was changed to eliminate or reduce the silver content of these coins. The copper-nickel "clad" dimes, quarters, and halves are composed of an outer layer of copper-nickel (75% copper and 25% nickel) bonded to an inner core of pure copper. The silver clad half dollar and dollar have an outer layer of 80% silver bonded to an inner core of 21% silver, with a total content of 40% silver.

Alloys are melted in crucibles and poured into molds to form ingots. The ingots are in the form of thin bars and vary in size according to the denomination of the coin. The width is sufficient to allow three coins to be cut from the strips.

The ingots are next put through rolling mills to reduce the thickness to required limits. The strips are then fed into cutting presses which cut circular blanks (planchets) of the approximate size of the finished coin. The blanks are run through annealing furnaces to soften them; next through tumbling barrels, rotating cylinders containing cleaning solutions which clean and burnish the metal, and finally into centrifugal drying machines.

The blanks are next fed into a milling machine which produces the raised or upset rim. The blank is now ready for the coining press.

The blank is held firmly by a collar, as it is struck, under heavy pressure varying from 40 tons for the one-cent pieces and dimes to 170 tons for silver dollars. Upper and lower dies impress the design on both sides of the coin. The pressure is sufficient to produce a raised surface level with that of the milled rim. The collar holding the blank for silver or clad coins is grooved. The pressure forces the metal into the grooves of the collar, producing the "reeding" on the finished coin.

How a Proof Coin Is Made

Selected dies are inspected for perfection and are highly polished and cleaned. They are again wiped clean or polished after every 15 to 25 impressions and are replaced frequently to avoid imperfections from worn dies. Coinage blanks are polished and cleaned to assure high quality in striking. They are then hand fed into the coinage press one at a time, each blank receiving two blows from the dies to bring up sharp, high relief details. The coinage operation is done at slow speed with extra pressure. Finished proofs are individually inspected and are handled by gloves or tongs. They also receive a final inspection by packers before being sonically sealed in special plastic cases.

Certain coins, including Lincoln cents, Buffalo nickels, Quarter Eagles, Half Eagles, Eagles and Double Eagles, between the years 1908 and 1916 were made with a matte or sandblast surface. Matte proofs have a dull frosted surface which is produced by special treatment after striking.

Mints and Mint Marks

In addition to the Philadelphia Mint, the U. S. Government has from time to time established branch mints in various parts of the country. At the present time a branch mint operates in Denver. Starting in 1968, proof sets and some of the regular coins are produced at the San Francisco Assay Office. The Denver Mint has operated since 1906. A mint was operated at New Orleans from 1838 to 1861 and again from 1879 to 1909. Mints were also in service at Carson City, Nevada, from 1870 to 1893; at Charlotte, North Carolina, from 1838 to 1861; at Dahlonega, Georgia, from 1838 to 1861; and at San Francisco from 1854 to 1955.

Coins struck at Philadelphia (except 1942 to 1945 five-cent pieces) do not carry a mint mark. The mint mark is found only on coins struck at the branch mints. It is a small letter, usually found on the reverse side. The Lincoln cent is one exception to the rule. All coins minted after 1967 have the mint mark on the obverse. The letters to signify the various mints are as follows:

"C" for Charlotte, North Carolina (on gold coins only).
"CC" for Carson City, Nevada.
"D" for Dahlonega, Georgia (gold coins only, 1838 to 1861).
"D" for Denver, Colorado (from 1906 to date).
"O" for New Orleans, Louisiana.
"P" for Philadelphia, Pennsylvania.
"S" for San Francisco, California.

The mint mark is of utmost importance to collectors due to the fact that the coinage at the branch mints has usually been much smaller than at Philadelphia and many of the branch mint pieces are very scarce.

Location of Mint Marks

Half Cents — All coined at Philadelphia, no mint mark.

Large Cents — All coined at Philadelphia, no mint mark.

Flying Eagle Cents — All coined at Philadelphia, no mint mark.

Indian Cents — 1908 and 1909, under the wreath on reverse side.

Lincoln Cents — Under the date.

Two Cents, nickel Three Cents — All coined at Philadelphia, no mint mark.

Three Cents Silver — All coined at Philadelphia, except 1851 New Orleans mint — reverse side.

Shield Nickels — All coined at Philadelphia, no mint mark.

Liberty Nickels — All coined at Philadelphia except 1912 S and D — reverse side to left of word CENTS.

Buffalo Nickels — Reverse side under words FIVE CENTS.

Jefferson Nickels — Reverse side at right of the building. Starting 1968, on obverse near date.

Jefferson Five-Cent Pieces (silver, 1942-1945 inclusive) — Above dome on reverse.

Half Dimes — Reverse side either within or below the wreath.

Dimes — Old types on reverse side below or within wreath; Mercury type (1916-1945) on the reverse to left of the fasces. Roosevelt type starting 1946, at left of base of torch. Starting 1968, on obverse above date.

Twenty Cents — Reverse, under the eagle.

Quarter Dollars — Old types on reverse under eagle; Standing Liberty type (after 1916) obverse to left of date; Washington type on reverse under eagle. Starting 1968, on obverse rght of ribbon.

Half Dollars — 1838-1839 above date; 1840-1915 on reverse below eagle. 1916 and some 1917 on obverse below TRUST; other 1917-1947 on lower left reverse below branch. Franklin, above liberty bell beam. Kennedy, left of olive branch near claw. Starting 1968, on obverse beneath truncation.

Dollars — Old types, on reverse under eagle; Peace type (1921 and after) on reverse near eagle's wing. Eisenhower type, above date.

Trade Dollars — On reverse under eagle.

Gold Dollars — Reverse under wreath.

Quarter Eagles ($2.50) — 1838 and 1839 over the date; other dates previous to 1907 on reverse under the eagle; Indian type (1908-29) on reverse lower left.

Three Dollar Pieces — Reverse under the wreath.

Half Eagles ($5.00) — Same as quarter eagles.

Eagles ($10.00) — Reverse under eagle; after 1907 at left of value.

Double Eagles ($20.00) — Old types on reverse under eagle; St. Gaudens (after 1907) above the date.

MINT MARKS

1908 and 1909 Indian Cents. San Francisco Mint only.

S or D found below date on obverse of Lincoln Cents.

Three-cent Silver, 1851 is only date this denomination produced at a branch mint. (New Orleans.)

[8]

MINT MARKS

Liberty Head Nickel 1912 S and D only, on reverse side.

Buffalo Nickel, on reverse side under "FIVE CENTS."

Jefferson Nickel, right of building 1938-42, 1946-64.

Jefferson 5c Silver 1942 to 1945. Above dome on reverse side.

Jefferson Nickel. Starting 1968, on obverse near date.

Half Dime. On reverse within, or below wreath.

Dime—old type. Reverse side. 1872-75-76 etc. Has mint mark within wreath also, as shown for half-dimes.

Barber Dime. Below wreath, reverse side.

Mercury Dime. On reverse to left of the fasces.

Roosevelt Dime 1946 to 1964

Roosevelt Dime. Starting 1968, on obverse above date.

Twenty-cent Piece. On reverse, under Eagle.

Quarter — old type. On reverse, under Eagle.

Barber Quarter. On reverse, under Eagle.

Standing Liberty Quarter. Very small mint mark found on obverse at left of date.

MINT MARKS

Washington Quarter, under eagle 1932-64.

Washington Quarter. Starting 1968, on obverse right of ribbon.

Half Dollar 1838-0 and 1839-0. On obverse, above date. (See page 66.)

Half Dollar, Barber and earlier types. On reverse, under Eagle.

Standing Liberty Half Dollar. 1916-1917 on obverse.

Standing Liberty Half Dollar. 1917 and later dates on reverse. (Either obverse or reverse on 1917.)

Franklin Half Dollar. Above liberty bell beam.

Kennedy Half Dollar, left of olive branch 1964 only.

Kennedy Half Dollar. Starting 1968, on obverse beneath truncation.

Silver Dollar—old types. On reverse, under Eagle.

Peace Type Dollar. On reverse, tip of eagle's wing.

Trade Dollar. On reverse, under Eagle.

Gold Dollar. On reverse, under wreath.

Quarter Eagle. 1838 and 1839 over date.

Quarter Eagle. On reverse under eagle until 1879.

MINT MARKS

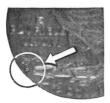

Quarter Eagle—Indian Type. On reverse, lower left.

Three-Dollar Gold. On reverse under wreath.

Eagle—old types. On reverse, under eagle.

Half Eagles. Mint marks found in the same position as Quarter Eagles.

Eagle — After 1907. At left of value.

Double Eagle—old types. On reverse under Eagle.

Double Eagle — After 1907. Above date.

DISTINGUISHING MARKS

The illustrations and explanations in this section will help the collector to identify certain well-known varieties.

HALF CENTS OF 1795-1796 SHOWING LOCATION OF POLE TO CAP
The end of the staff or pole lies parallel with the line of the bust, which is pointed. The die-maker, probably through error, omitted the pole on some of the dies of 1795 and 1796.

Pole to Cap   No Pole to Cap

Stemless Wreath

Stems to Wreath

STEMLESS WREATH VARIETY OF HALF CENTS AND LARGE CENTS
Observe the reverse side for this variety. Illustrations at left show both stemless and stems to wreath types for easy comparison—stemless wreath found on 1804, 1805, 1806, Half cents. 1797, 1802, 1803 Large cents.

1804 HALF CENT PROTRUDING TONGUE OR SPIKED CHIN VARIETY

DISTINGUISHING MARKS

Plain 4   Crosslet 4

Details showing differences in 1804 plain 4 and crosslet 4. Note serif on horizontal bar of figure 4 as shown at right.

THE 1856 FLYING EAGLE CENT
Collectors are advised to inspect any 1856 Flying Eagle cent carefully.

A few tests will aid in establishing genuineness of this cent, as follows:

THE DATE
The 6 in the date should be as illustrated. If the lower half is thick, it is probably an altered 1858. A magnifying glass will often reveal poor workmanship.

The figure 5 slants slightly to the right on a genuine 1856. The vertical bar points to the center of the ball just beneath. On the 1858,

this bar points *outside* the ball. (Compare the two illustrations.)

THE LEGEND
The center of the O in OF is crude and almost squared on the genuine 1856, but on the large letter 1858 it is rounded.

The letters A and M in America are joined in both the 1856 and large letter 1858, but they join at a slight angle on the 1856, while the bottom of the letters form a smooth curve on the 1858 large letter cent.

Large Letters

Small Letters

1858 FLYING EAGLE CENT

Letters A and M in the word AMERICA are joined on the LARGE LETTER variety. They are separated on the SMALL LETTER variety.

DISTINGUISHING MARKS

1864 BRONZE INDIAN HEAD CENT WITH "L" ON RIBBON

A small "L," the initial of the designer Longacre, was added to the Indian design late in 1864 and was continued through 1909. For coins in less than fine condition, this small letter will often be worn away. The point of the bust is rounded on the 1864 variety without "L"; pointed on the variety with "L." The initial must be visible, however, for the 1864 variety to bring the higher premium. If the coin is turned slightly so that the Indian faces the observer, the highlighted details will usually appear to better advantage.

Small Motto

Large Motto

TWO CENTS OF 1864

Details explain the differences in these two well-known varieties. On the obverse, D in God is narrow on the large motto. The stem to the leaf shows plainly on the small motto variety. There is no stem on the large motto coin. First T in TRUST, small motto variety, is closer to ribbon crease at left.

(At top) 1909 Initials appear on reverse. (At right) Initials appear beneath shoulder, 1918 and later.

LINCOLN CENTS SHOWING LOCATION OF INITIALS V D B

1918-S QUARTER 8 OVER 7

A variety of this kind is rarely found in coinage of the twentieth century.

DISTINGUISHING MARKS

1938D over S Nickel Variety

Large Date Cent
1960

Small Date Cent
1960

1942 Dime
with 2 over 1
(Philadelphia Mint)

1955 Cent Error
"Double Die" Obverse

CONDITION OF COINS

FAIR. Excessive wear, but coin has sufficient design and letters to be easily identified.

G. or GOOD. All of design, every feature and legend must be plain and date clear.

V. G. or VERY GOOD. Features all clear and bold. Better than good, but not quite fine.

F. or FINE. Obviously a circulated coin but little wear. Mint lustre gone. All letters in LIBERTY and mottoes clear.

V. FINE or VERY FINE. Shows enough wear on high spots to be noticable. Still retains enough lustre to be desirable.

EX. FINE or EXTREMELY FINE. Slightly circulated with some lustre but faint evidence of wear.

UNC. or UNCIRCULATED. New. Regular mint striking, but never placed in circulation. Older pieces may be tarnished or "toned."

PF. or PROOF. Coins with mirrorlike surface, specially struck for collectors. Also sandblast and matte proof. *See Page 7.*

Coins dated before 1968 from branch mints having a mirrorlike surface are not proofs but are first strikings of new dies.

IMPORTANT: Coins in any condition with defects, such as those which are bent, corroded, scratched, holed, nicked, stained, oxidized, mutilated, or with other imperfections, are worth less than if free of these defects.

Preserving and Cleaning Coins

Most numismatists will tell you to "never clean a coin" and it is good advice; however, every collector tries to clean a coin sooner or later, so we are passing on a few tips here.

In the first place some effort should be made to keep uncirculated and proof coins bright so they won't need cleaning. Tarnish on a coin is purely a chemical process caused by oxygen in the air acting on the metal or by chemicals with which the coin comes in contact. One of the commonest chemicals causing tarnish is sulphur; most paper, with the exception of specially manufactured "sulphur-free" kinds, contains sulphur due to the sulphuric acid that is used in paper manufacture. Therefore do not wrap coins in ordinary paper; also keep uncirculated and proof coins away from rubber bands (a rubber band placed on a silver coin for a few days will produce a black stripe on the coin where the band touched).

The utmost in protection is received by wrapping the coin in lead or aluminum foil and then placing it in a tarnish-proof envelope (both items are sold by coin dealers).

Many coins become marred by careless handling. Always hold the coin by the edge. The accompanying illustration shows the right and wrong way to handle numismatic specimens. It is a breach of numismatic etiquette to handle another collector's coin except by the edge, even if it is not an uncirculated or proof piece.

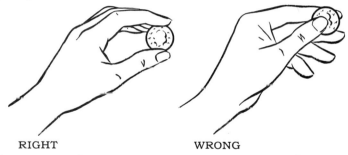

RIGHT   WRONG

If you must satisfy the urge to try to clean coins, experiment first with some ordinary coins.

Modern silver coins can often be cleaned with a paste consisting of baking soda and water without harming the coin. Hold about a teaspoonful of paste in the palm of one hand. Work the coin gently into the paste with the other hand. Rinse the coin in clear water and dry with a clean blotter. DO NOT use kitchen cleanser, silver polish, a pencil eraser or other abrasives on any coins.

Copper and bronze coins are very difficult to clean. Scrubbing with an abrasive makes the high parts of the coin bright while the other parts will look dirtier than ever, giving the piece a very unnatural appearance that considerably lessens its value in the numismatic market. The use of acids and buffing wheels also produces an unnatural appearance.

No amount of scrubbing or cleaning, or the use of acids or buffers, will restore the original mint lustre to a coin.

Starting a Collection

One may start a collection of United States coins with very little expense by systematically assembling the various dates and mint marks of all the types and denominations that are now in general circulation. Whitman's coin folders make this possible.

With the exception of the 50¢ paid for the coin folder, collecting coins received in everyday business transactions entails no expense whatever; a Jefferson nickel taken out of circulation, for example, can always be spent for 5 cents if the occasion arrives. Filling a board or two out of circulation is probably the best method of determining whether coin collecting appeals to you. Not everyone can be a successful coin collector. It requires patience, intelligence of a high order, and a certain desire to know the meaning behind a lot of things that at first glance and to the ordinary mortal appear meaningless. You may not be cut out to be a collector but you'll never know until you look further into the subject, and if by the time a board or two of coins are collected you have no burning desire to acquire many more different coins, you will probably never be a collector. However, the chances are that you will be, because if you have read this far in this book it shows that you are interested in the subject.

Although forming a collection "out-of-circulation" is the least expensive method, it is possible not only to have a lot of fun with such a collection but also to profit to a certain degree. The cheapest coins to collect are the current Lincoln head cents. Many dates can be found in circulation. There are scores of coins in circulation dated after 1930 that are worth a premium to collectors. It is possible to collect hundreds of different United States coins out of general circulation.

Perfection is the goal of every endeavor and coin collecting is no exception. After a board has been filled with circulated specimens the next step will be to replace pieces with coins in uncirculated condition; or perhaps to start collecting the obsolete series; in either case it will be necessary to purchase some coins from dealers or other collectors. The most logical way to keep abreast with the market, or obtain the addresses of the country's leading dealers, is to subscribe to one or more of the trade publications (see page 5 for list of the coin magazines). These magazines carry advertisements of various dealers listing coins for sale. Moreover, through this source the beginner may obtain price lists and catalogs from the dealers.

There are several good reference books available at reasonable prices which will be helpful to the collector who wishes to know more about U. S. coins and paper money. The GUIDE BOOK OF U. S. COINS (Red Book) is an expanded version of THE HANDBOOK. It lists retail values of all regular U. S. coins and also lists all coins of the U. S. Colonial period and private and territorial gold coins.

Most coin, book and hobby dealers can supply the following titles:

    GUIDE BOOK OF U. S COINS — Yeoman
    U. S COMMEMORATIVE COINAGE — Slabaugh
    SELECTIONS FROM THE NUMISMATIST, Vol. I — U. S. COINS
    U. S. PATTERN, EXPERIMENTAL & TRIAL PIECES — Judd
    PATRIOTIC CIVIL WAR TOKENS — Fuld
    GUIDE TO CIVIL WAR STORE CARDS — Fuld
    THE FANTASTIC 1804 DOLLAR — Newman & Bressett
    GUIDE BOOK OF MODERN U.S. CURRENCY — Shafer
    CONFEDERATE STATES PAPER MONEY — Slabaugh
    U. S. FRACTIONAL CURRENCY — Rothert
    BUYING AND SELLING U. S. COINS — Bressett & Yeoman

JOIN A COIN CLUB

A beginner should join a "coin club" if he is fortunate enough to live in a city which has one. The association with more experienced collectors will be of great benefit. Practically all the larger cities have one or more clubs and they are being rapidly organized in the smaller towns. The publications mentioned on page 5 carry lists of coin clubs and special events such as coin shows and conventions.

Abbreviations

Like most businesses the coin trade has developed a number of abbreviations which are used generally in magazine advertising to conserve space in listing coins. To many a beginner, reading such an advertisement for the first time, it is difficult to understand. However, the abbreviations are not numerous and they can be quickly mastered. Some of the abbreviations are peculiar to particular types or denominations and are mentioned in this book in their respective places. The more general abbreviations are:

Obv. or Ob. — Obverse. The "heads" side of a coin.

Rev., Rx., or R. — Reverse. The "tails" side of a coin.

Var., Vars. — Variety, Varieties.

Ty. or T. — Type. (A frequent abbreviation is N.T. or O.T., meaning new type or old type.)

Lib. — Liberty.

Lge. or Lg. — Large.

Sm. — Small.

The condition of the coin is the most frequently abbreviated item. The common condition abbreviations are:

Pr. or Pf. — Proof.

Unc., Uncir., or U. — Uncirculated.

E.F., X.F., or Ex.F. — Extremely Fine. (Also Extra Fine.)

V.F. — Very Fine. (The "V" is sometimes used to denote "very" in other cases, such as very rare, very scarce.)

V.G. or V.Gd. — Very Good.

G. or Gd. — Good.

Fr. — Fair.

Brill., or Bril. — Brilliant.

An example of an abbreviated coin listing is as follows:

Standing Liberty Quarters
1917-S Var. 2, VG, Sc........$0.00

The figures "1917" stand for the year of coinage, "S" for the San Francisco mint mark, "Var. 2" means the piece is of the second variety, "VG" is the condition, "Sc." meaning the piece is scarce. The price which follows is the value of the coin.

UNITED STATES PAPER MONEY

Paper money issued by the United States government is collected widely in this country. The first issue of "greenbacks" was made in 1861; paper money was not issued by our government for circulation prior to that date. Collectors of U.S. notes prefer them in crisp, new condition; therefore the old style large-sized notes in worn condition are usually worth very little more than face value.

Before the issuance of the first U.S. government paper money, many banks throughout the country issued their own currency. These issues are commonly referred to as "broken bank notes" although that is somewhat of a misnomer as many of the banks did not "go broke" (a few are still in existence) and redeemed their paper money issues. There are thousands of varieties of these notes in existence, most of which are very common and worth from 25¢ to 50¢ each. Before and during the American Revolution the various individual states and the Continental Congress issued paper money. The commoner varieties of these Colonial notes are worth from $1.00 to $3.00; a few are quite rare.

U. S. HALF CENTS

Issued from 1793 through 1857

Metal: Copper.

All half cents are really scarce, but the series has never enjoyed the popularity of some of the other series, hence the more common dates of half cents are not extremely valuable.

The series does, however, contain a number of rarities, 1796 being the rarest date. The dates 1840, 1841, 1842, 1843, 1844, 1845, 1846, 1847, 1848, 1849 small date, and 1852 were issued in proof only, and in two varieties. Those with the ten large berries and one small berry on the reverse are called the "originals" and those with eleven small berries on the reverse are termed "restrikes." A restrike is an impression made from genuine dies but at a later time than the date shown on the coin. It is said that eighteen specimens of both varieties of the above mentioned dates were struck.

Terms used in describing Half Cents:

Lettered Edge (1793, 1794, 1795, and 1797)—The words "Two Hundred for a Dollar" are found on the edge of some or all varieties of these dates.

Pole to Cap (or no pole to cap) — All varieties of the 1794 have a "pole to cap," that is, the pole shows beside the head of Liberty. The years 1795 and 1796 are found with the pole and also "without" a pole.

Stemless Wreath; Stems to Wreath (1804, 1805, and 1806.) — On some of the reverses of these dates the wreath has stems; on others the wreath does not have stems. (See page 11.)

Crosslet 4; Plain 4 — On those of 1804 only. The "4" in the date appears on some varieties with a serif; that is known as the "crosslet 4." The variety without serif is known as the "plain 4." There is also a variety of the 1804 known as the "spiked chin" or "protruding tongue" on which Liberty appears to be sticking out her tongue. (See page 11.)

Overdates — An overdate is the result of using a die of a previous year and re-cutting the new date over the old figures. In the half cent series, the following overdates are found: 1802 over 1800; 1808 over 7; 1809 over 6. A variety of 1797 has a "1 over 1" which is actually not an overdate but an error in die cutting — the engraver rather than cut a new die merely cut another figure 1.

The following abbreviations are found in numismatic literature referring to half cents.

Pl. — plain; *Let.* — lettered; *Ed.* — edge; *Perf.* — perfect; *Ov.* — over; *Sm.* — small; *Lg.* — large.

LIBERTY CAP TYPE 1793-1797

FAIR—*Clear enough to identify.*

GOOD—*Outline of bust clear, no details. Date readable. Reverse lettering incomplete.*

VERY GOOD—*Some hair details. Reverse lettering complete.*

FINE—*Most of hair detail shows.*

Head facing left 1793

	Quan. Minted	Fair	Good	V. Good	Fine
1793	35,334	$75.00	$125.00	$185.00	$375.00

HALF CENTS

Head facing
right
1794-1797

	Quan. Minted	Fair	Good	V. Good	Fine
1794	81,600	$ 25.00	$ 40.00	$ 60.00	$ 95.00
1795	134,600	25.00	40.00	60.00	95.00
1796 Pole to cap	5,090	245.00	480.00	750.00	1450.00
No pole to cap	1,390	325.00	700.00	1050.00	1650.00
1797 Lettered edge	} 119,214	55.00	110.00	175.00	285.00
Plain edge		17.50	32.50	47.50	80.00

DRAPED BUST TYPE 1800-1808

FAIR—*Clear enough to identify.*
GOOD—*Bust outline clear, no details, date readable. Reverse lettering worn and incomplete.*
VERY GOOD—*Some drapery shows. Date and legends complete.*
FINE—*Shoulder drapery and hair over brow worn smooth.*

1800	211,530	3.50	6.50	9.25	14.00
1802	14,366	27.50	50.00	80.00	125.00
1803	97,900	3.50	7.00	10.00	16.00
1804	1,055,312	3.50	6.00	9.00	12.00
1805	814,464	3.50	6.00	9.25	12.50
1806	356,000	3.50	6.00	9.25	12.50
1807	476,000	3.50	6.00	9.25	12.50
1808 8 over 7	} 400,000	12.50	22.50	37.00	57.50
Normal date		3.50	6.25	9.00	12.00

CLASSIC HEAD TYPE 1809-1836

GOOD—*LIBERTY only partly visible on hair band. Lettering, date, stars, worn but visible.*
VERY GOOD—*LIBERTY entirely visible on hair band. Lower curls worn.*
FINE—*Only part wear on LIBERTY and hair at top worn in spots.*

1809 9 over 6	} 1,154,572	3.00	6.00	9.00	12.50
Normal date		3.00	5.50	7.25	10.50

HALF CENTS

	Quan. Minted	Good	V. Good	Fine	Proof
1810	215,000	$ 6.00	$10.00	$19.00	
1811	63,140	20.00	30.00	42.50	
1825	63,000	5.50	6.75	8.00	
1826	234,000	5.50	6.75	8.00	
1828	606,000	5.25	6.25	7.25	
1829	487,000	5.25	6.25	7.25	
1831 Original (Large berries on wreath)	2,200				$550.00
Restrike (Small berries on wreath)					425.00
1832	*estimated 154,000	5.25	6.25	8.50	
1833	*estimated 120,000	5.25	6.25	8.50	
1834	*estimated 141,000	5.25	6.25	8.50	
1835	*estimated 398,000	5.25	6.25	8.50	
1836 Original (Large berries on wreath)					500.00
Restrike (Small berries on wreath)					500.00

*The figures given here are thought to be correct, although official mint records give the same quantities for 1833-36 rather than 1832-35.

No half cents were struck in 1837. Because of the great need for small change, however, a large number of tokens similar in size to current half cents and large cents were issued privately by businessmen who needed them in commerce. One of the most popular pieces is listed and illustrated below.

1837 Token.......................... 10.00   14.00   23.00

BRAIDED HAIR TYPE 1840-1857

1840 Original (Large berries on wreath)	375.00
Restrike (Small berries on wreath)	375.00
1841 Original (Large berries)	375.00
Restrike (Small berries)	375.00
1842 Original (Large berries)	375.00
Restrike (Small berries)	375.00

HALF CENTS

	Proof
1843 Original (Large berries)	$375.00
Restrike (Small berries)	375.00
1844 Original (Large berries,	375.00
Restrike (Small berries)	375.00
1845 Original (Large berries)	375.00
Restrike (Small berries)	375.00
1846 Original (Large berries)	375.00
Restrike (Small berries)	375.00
1847 Original (Large berries)	375.00
Restrike (Small berries)	375.00
1848 Original (Large berries)	375.00
Restrike (Small berries)	375.00
1849 Small date, original (Large berries)	375.00
Small date, restrike (Small berries)	375.00

VERY GOOD—*Beads uniformly distinct. Hairlines show in spots.*
FINE—*Hairlines above ear worn. Beads sharp.*
VERY FINE—*Lowest curl shows wear, hair otherwise distinct.*

	Quan. Minted	V. Good	Fine	V. Fine
1849 Large date	39,864	$7.50	$12.50	$19.00
1850	39,812	6.50	9.50	16.50
1851	147,672	5.50	8.00	12.50
				Proof
1852 Original (Large berries)				
Restrike (Small berries)				350.00
		V. Good	Fine	V. Fine
1853	129,694	5.50	8.00	12.50
1854	55,358	5.50	8.00	12.50
1855	56,500	5.50	8.00	12.50
1856	40,430	5.50	8.00	12.50
1857	35,180	9.00	16.00	25.00

U. S. LARGE COPPER CENTS
Issued from 1793 through 1857

A very interesting and popular series; more has been written about these coins than any other United States series. They were coined in every year during the period 1793 to 1857 except 1815. There are 60 different die varieties of the cents of 1794 and most of the other dates have a dozen or more. These variations are sometimes slight, often being merely the position of a leaf in the wreath or the spacing of the figures of the date.

In advertisements listing large cents, it is not uncommon to read such notations as, "1807 S. 273" or "D. 203." These refer to die varieties; "S" denoting Sheldon, "D" for Doughty. Various numismatic students have made a study of the varieties of various years and the varieties are named after these students; Crosby for 1793, Chapman for 1794, Doughty for 1795, 1797 to 1814 inclusive, Clapp for 1798; Newcomb 1801, 1802 and 1803, Sheldon for 1793-1814, and Newcomb for the years 1816 to 1857 inclusive. However, most collectors are content to acquire just one of each date, and leave the collecting of die varieties to the specialist.

Recommended Reference Books

For those who care to go into the detail study of large cent varieties the following books are recommended:
"The Cents and Half Cents of 1793" by S. S. Crosby.
"The Cents of 1794" by S. H. Chapman.
"United States Cents" by Francis W. Doughty.
"Cents of 1798 and 1799" by Geo. Clapp.
"Cents of 1801, 1802 and 1803" by Newcomb.
"United States Copper Cents 1816-1857" by Newcomb.
"Cents 1795, 1796, 1797 and 1800" by Clapp.
"Penny Whimsy" by Sheldon, Paschal and Breen (1793-1814).

Condition Is Important

Condition plays a big part in the value of a large cent, especially the early dates. Evidence of this is brought out by a comparison of the lowest grade price with the highest in the premium values following.

Rare Dates Often Faked

In collecting large cents these three dates especially should be purchased from reliable dealers only who will guarantee the genuineness of the coins. The 1793 is frequently "electrotyped." An electrotype can generally be determined by examining the edge to determine if two shells have been placed together. Cents of 1799 will be found "electrotyped" and also made by altering the "8" of the more common 1798 to a "9." An examination of a suspicious piece under a magnifying glass will generally reveal the alteration. Fake cents of 1804 are made by altering most any of the other dates of the same general type, an 1801 being most frequently used. A quick way to check this point is to determine whether the "O" in the date is directly opposite the "O" in OF on the reverse. The peculiarity is found on genuine cents of 1804 and if the piece has been made by altering another date the cipher and the O will not be exactly opposite.

LARGE CENTS

Restrike of the 1804 Cent

A fake 1804 was manufactured about the year 1860 to satisfy the demand for this rare date. This piece is known as the "restrike" but fortunately for collectors it was a patchwork job and easily distinguished from a genuine 1804 cent. An old rusty die was used for the obverse which makes the field of the coin pitted and a die of the year 1820, which is much different from an 1804, was used for the reverse. To aid collectors, an illustration of 1804 restrike is shown here.

Terms Used in Describing Large Cents

Chain Type — The first type of year 1793, has an endless chain of links on the reverse.

Lettered Edge — Some 1793, 1794 and 1795 cents have lettering, "One Hundred for a Dollar" on the edge.

Broken Die — Cracks or lumps on the coin caused by the die breaking or cracking.

Stemless Wreath — See Half Cents.

Wreaths to Stems — See Half Cents.

Crosslet and Plain 4 — See Half Cents.

Overdate — See Half Cents.

The terms, "wide date," "compact date," "large letters," "small letters," "plain hair cord," "beaded hair cord," "large fraction," "small fraction," etc., are also used and are self-explanatory.

The following abbreviations are used in describing large cents:

Let. Ed. — lettered edge; *Lib.* — liberty; *Pl. Ed.* — plain edge; *Ov.* — over; *Perf.* — perfect; *Frac.* — fraction; *Sm.* — small; *Lg.* — large; *Up.* — upright; *Sl.* — slanting.

FLOWING HAIR, CHAIN TYPE REVERSE 1793

FAIR—Date and devices clear enough to identify.

GOOD—Lettering worn but readable. Bust has no detail.

VERY GOOD—Date and lettering distinct, some details of head visible.

FINE—About half of hair, etc. details show.

	Quan. Minted	Fair	Good	V. Good	Fine
1793 AMERI. in legend	36,103	$95.00	$200.00	$325.00	$550.00
AMERICA		80.00	150.00	285.00	465.00

LARGE CENTS

FLOWING HAIR, WREATH TYPE REVERSE 1793

→
Strawberry
Sprig
Variety

	Quan. Minted	Fair	Good	V. Good	Fine
1793 Wreath type	63,353	$65.00	$110.00	$185.00	$325.00
1793 Strawberry sprig var. (4 known)					

LIBERTY CAP TYPE 1793-1796

1793 Liberty cap	11,056	165.00	280.00	500.00	900.00
1794	918,521	8.00	16.00	25.00	40.00
1795 Plain edge	82,000	6.00	13.50	23.00	37.50
Lettered edge	456,500	15.00	24.00	37.50	70.00
1796 Liberty cap	109,825	12.50	22.00	35.00	65.00

DRAPED BUST TYPE 1796-1807

FAIR—*Clear enough to identify.*

GOOD—*Lettering worn, but clear; date clear. Bust lacks details.*

V. GOOD—*Drapery partly visible. Less wear in date and lettering.*

FINE—*Hair over brow is smooth, some detail showing elsewhere.*

1796 Draped Bust	363,375	11.00	20.00	32.50	47.50
1797 Normal wreath	} 897,510	5.00	9.00	14.00	23.00
Stemless wreath		12.00	30.00	50.00	75.00
1798 8 over 7	} 979,700	8.00	15.00	27.50	47.50
Normal date		3.00	6.00	10.00	17.00
1799 (Beware of altered date)					
9 over 8	} 904,585	90.00	165.00	310.00	550.00
Normal date		85.00	150.00	285.00	525.00
1800	2,822,175	3.00	5.00	7.00	16.00
1801	1,362,837	3.00	5.00	7.00	16.00
1802	3,435,100	1.75	3.50	5.50	13.00

LARGE CENTS

	Quan. Minted	Fair	Good	V. Good	Fine
1803	2,471,353	$ 2.25	$ 4.00	$ 6.00	$ 13.00
1804 Original	756,838	57.50	100.00	175.00	250.00
So-called "Mint Restrike" (See page 23)					
1805	941,116	2.25	5.00	8.50	16.00
1806	348,000	5.00	12.00	19.00	36.00
1807 7 over 6	}727,221	2.25	4.50	7.50	14.00
Normal date		2.25	4.50	7.50	14.00

CLASSIC HEAD TYPE 1808-1814

FAIR—*Details clear enough to identify.*

GOOD—*Legends, stars, date worn, but plain.*

V. GOOD—*LIBERTY all readable. Ear shows. Details worn but plain.*

FINE—*Hair on forehead and before ear nearly smooth. Ear and hair under ear sharp.*

1808	1,109,000	3.50	8.25	14.00	25.00
1809	222,867	16.00	35.00	55.00	100.00
1810	1,458,500	3.00	6.50	10.50	18.00
1811	218,025	14.00	21.00	33.50	80.00
1812	1,075,500	2.50	6.00	9.50	16.00
1813	418,000	5.00	12.00	20.00	36.00
1814	357,830	3.00	6.50	10.50	18.00

CORONET TYPE 1816-1857

GOOD—*Head details partly visible. Even wear in date and legends.*

V. GOOD—*LIBERTY, date, stars, legends clear. Part of hair cord visible.*

FINE—*All hairlines show. Hair cords show uniformly.*

	Quan. Minted	Good	V. Good	Fine
1816	2,820,982	2.75	3.75	6.00
1817	3,948,400	2.00	3.00	5.00
1818	3,167,000	2.00	3.00	5.00
1819	2,671,000	2.00	3.00	5.00
1820	4,407,550	2.00	3.00	5.00
1821	389,000	6.50	11.00	20.00
1822	2,072,339	2.00	3.75	5.50
1823	855,730	10.00	17.00	30.00
1824	1,262,000	3.00	4.75	7.50
1825	1,461,100	2.75	4.25	7.00
1826	1,517,425	2.75	4.25	7.00
1827	2,357,732	2.50	3.50	6.00
1828	2,260,624	2.50	3.25	5.50
1829	1,414,500	2.50	3.25	5.50
1830	1,711,500	2.50	3.25	5.50

LARGE CENTS

	Quan. Minted	Good	V. Good	Fine
1831	3,359,260	$ 2.00	$ 3.00	$ 4.50
1832	2,362,000	2.00	3.00	4.50
1833	2,739,000	2.00	3.00	4.50
1834	1,855,100	2.25	3.50	6.50
1835	3,878,400	2.00	2.75	5.00
1836	2,111,000	2.00	2.75	5.00
1837	5,558,300	2.00	2.75	4.50
1838	6,370,200	2.00	2.75	4.00
1839 9 over 6	}3,128,661	60.00	90.00	160.00
Normal date		3.25	5.50	10.00

1840	2,462,700	2.00	2.75	4.50
1841	1,597,367	2.00	2.75	4.50
1842	2,383,390	2.00	2.75	4.50
1843	2,428,320	2.00	2.75	4.50
1844	2,398,752	1.65	1.85	2.50
1845	3,894,804	1.65	1.85	2.50
1846	4,120,800	1.65	1.85	2.50
1847	6,183,669	1.65	1.85	2.50
1848	6,415,799	1.65	1.85	2.50
1849	4,178,500	1.65	1.85	2.50
1850	4,426,844	1.65	1.85	2.50
1851	9,889,707	1.65	1.85	2.50
1852	5,063,094	1.65	1.85	2.50
1853	6,641,131	1.65	1.85	2.50
1854	4,236,156	1.65	1.85	2.50
1855	1,574,829	2.25	2.75	4.00
1856	2,690,463	1.65	1.85	2.50
1857	333,456	11.00	14.00	18.00

Only a small fraction of the Large Cents issued over a period of 64 years are available. It is an interesting fact that the Treasury Department made a special effort to retire these coins in 1857. They were considered too large for use in business transactions. The smaller coin was considerably more popular. Details of exchange are covered in a circular issued by the mint April 27, 1857.

Following are excerpts from this regulation:

"1. On and after the twenty-fifth day of May next, applications may be made at the mint for cents of the new issue in exchange for . . . the Spanish Pillar Dollar, and the Mexican Dollar . . . or in exchange for the copper cents heretofore issued.

2. The silver or copper coins must be in even sums of five dollars . . . not exceeding fifty dollars. . . ."

This bulletin will help us to understand what has become of a great many large copper cents.

SMALL CENTS
Authorized for Circulation in 1857
FLYING EAGLE TYPE 1856-1858

The first issue of the present small-sized cent. Those of 1856 are generally considered to be patterns but were issued in rather large number for a pattern coin. It is said that there were about 1,000 pieces struck of the commonest variety of the 1856 (copper-nickel or thick planchet, tobacco wreath on reverse). In all there are twelve varieties of the 1856. Cents of the flying eagle type dated 1857 and 1858 are common, except in proof condition; in that condition they are quite expensive. "United States of America" on the flying eagle cent of 1858 comes in two sizes of letters. These types are known as "small letters" and "large letters" (abbreviated, S.L. and L.L.). On the small letter variety the A and M in America are separated; the large letter variety shows these two letters joined at the base.

Fake 1856's are made by altering an 1858. Such species are recognized by the thickness of the lower half of the manufactured "6." (See page 12.)

GOOD—All details worn, but readable.

V. GOOD—Feather details and eye of Eagle are evident, but worn.

FINE—Eagle head details and feather tips sharp.

V. FINE—Eagle's eye very bold. Feather ends on right wing worn smooth, considerable detail in right wing and tail.

	Quan. Minted	Good	V. Good	Fine	V. Fine	Unc.	Proof
1856		$365.00	$450.00	$600.00	$745.00	$1350.00	$1675.00
1857	17,450,000	2.75	3.50	5.00	7.25	62.50	
1858 All Kinds	24,600,000						
Large Letters		2.75	3.50	6.00	8.50	66.00	
Small Letters		2.75	3.50	6.00	8.50	66.00	

INDIAN HEAD TYPE 1859-1909

Those of the years 1859 to 1863 were struck in copper-nickel and are commonly termed "white cents" because the metal is of lighter color. In 1864 the metal was changed to the present-used bronze, although copper-nickel cents of 1864 were struck, too. Soon after the change of metal the initial "L," for the engraver Longacre, was placed on the ribbon of the headdress. The "L" variety was struck in smaller quantity than the earlier variety without it, and is therefore quite rare. The "L" appears on the ribbon under the last feather of the headdress on *all* other dates from 1865 to 1909. (See page 13.)

Abbreviations peculiar to this series are:

IH. or IND. HD. — Indian Head.

C-N or Cop.-Nic. — Copper-nickel.

Note: Indian head cents having the date 1858 were not struck for circulation. They are patterns.

SMALL CENTS
Variety 1 — Copper-nickel, laurel wreath reverse 1859

GOOD—*No LIBERTY visible.*
V. GOOD—*At least half of LIBERTY readable.*
FINE—*LIBERTY completely visible.*
V. FINE—*Slight but even wear on LIBERTY.*

Without shield at top of
wreath on reverse

	Quan. Minted	Good	V. Good	Fine	V. Fine
1859 Indian Head...........36,400,000		$1.25	$1.75	$3.25	$5.75

Variety 2 — Copper-nickel, oak wreath with shield 1860-1864

With shield
on reverse

1860.....................20,566,000	1.25	1.75	2.75	4.50
1861.....................10,100,000	3.00	4.25	6.00	8.25
1862.....................28,075,000	.90	1.25	1.85	2.85
1863.....................49,840,000	.80	1.15	1.75	2.75
1864 Cop.-Nic. 13,740,000	2.00	3.00	4.25	6.25

Variety 3 — Bronze 1864-1909

1864 Bronze (no L on ribbon)) $39,233,714	.85	1.50	2.50	5.00
1864 with L (see p. 13) ....)	7.00	12.00	25.00	37.50
1865.....................35,429,286	.90	1.25	2.50	4.00
1866......................9,826,500	4.00	6.00	10.00	20.00
1867......................9,821,000	4.00	6.00	10.00	20.00
1868.....................10,266,500	4.00	6.00	10.00	20.00
1869......................6,420,000	7.00	11.50	20.00	32.50
1870......................5,275,000	6.50	9.50	17.50	25.00
1871......................3,929,500	8.00	12.50	20.00	32.50
1872......................4,042,000	9.50	15.00	22.50	36.00
1873.....................11,676,500	2.00	3.00	5.25	9.00
1874.....................14,187,500	2.00	3.00	5.25	9.00
1875.....................13,528,000	2.00	3.00	5.25	9.00
1876......................7,944,000	3.00	4.25	7.50	12.50
1877........................852,500	42.50	62.50	90.00	130.00
1878......................5,799,850	3.25	4.50	7.75	12.50
1879.....................16,231,200	.75	1.10	2.00	3.25
1880.....................38,964,955	.25	.35	.75	1.25
1881.....................39,211,575	.25	.35	.75	1.25
1882.....................38,581,100	.25	.35	.75	1.25
1883.....................45,598,109	.25	.35	.75	1.25

SMALL CENTS

	Quan. Minted	Good	V. Good	Fine	V. Fine
1884	23,261,742	$ .50	$ .85	$1.50	$2.75
1885	11,765,384	1.50	2.25	4.00	6.00
1886	17,654,290	.50	.85	1.50	2.75
1887	45,226,483	.20	.25	.45	.90
1888	37,494,414	.20	.25	.45	.90
1889	48,869,361	.20	.25	.45	.90
1890	57,182,854	.20	.25	.45	.90
1891	47,072,350	.20	.25	.45	.90
1892	37,649,832	.20	.25	.45	.90
1893	46,642,195	.20	.25	.45	.90
1894	16,752,132	.60	.85	1.75	3.75
1895	38,343,636	.20	.25	.45	.90
1896	39,057,293	.20	.25	.45	.90
1897	50,466,330	.20	.25	.45	.90
1898	49,823,079	.20	.25	.45	.90
1899	53,600,031	.20	.25	.45	.90
1900	66,833,764	.15	.20	.30	.50
1901	79,611,143	.15	.20	.30	.50
1902	87,376,722	.15	.20	.30	.50
1903	85,094,493	.15	.20	.30	.50
1904	61,328,015	.15	.20	.30	.50
1905	80,719,163	.15	.20	.30	.50
1906	96,022,255	.15	.20	.30	.50
1907	108,138,618	.15	.20	.30	.50
1908	32,327,987	.20	.25	.40	.70
1908S	1,115,000	7.75	9.50	12.00	16.50
1909 Indian	14,370,645	.30	.45	.75	1.00
1909S Indian	309,000	25.00	37.50	45.00	57.50

LINCOLN TYPE, WHEAT EARS REVERSE
1909-1958
Variety 1 — Bronze 1909-1942

The first year of the Lincoln cent, 1909, comes with or without the small letters "VDB" on the reverse near the lower edge. These letters are the initials of the designer, Victor D. Brenner. There was some protest about the placing of the initials on the coin and they were removed, only to be replaced on the cents of 1918 and thereafter in new position, under Lincoln's bust, in letters so small that an uncirculated piece is often necessary for examination to find it.

GOOD—Date worn but apparent. Lines in wheat ears missing.

V. GOOD—Lines show in upper wheat ears.

FINE—Wheat lines worn but visible.

V. FINE—Cheek and jaw bones worn but separated. No worn spots on wheat ears.

EXTRA FINE—Slight wear. All details sharp.

	Quan. Minted	Good	V. Good	Fine	V. Fine
1909 Lincoln Head	72,702,618	$ .03	$ .04	$ .07	$ .20
1909 V.D.B. (See page 13)	27,995,000	.30	.40	.50	.70
1909S	1,825,000	10.00	11.00	13.00	15.00
1909S V.D.B.	484,000	57.50	62.50	70.00	85.00
1910	146,801,218	.02	.03	.07	.15
1910S	6,045,000	1.50	1.85	2.75	3.75
1911	101,177,787	.02	.03	.07	.20

LINCOLN CENTS

	Quan. Minted	Good	V. Good	Fine	V. Fine
1911D.....................12,672,000		$ .65	$ .95	$1.50	$2.25
1911S......................4,026,000		4.00	4.50	6.00	8.50
1912.......................68,153,060		.03	.04	.08	.25
1912D.....................10,411,000		.60	.85	1.60	3.15
1912S......................4,431,000		2.00	2.50	3.00	5.25
1913.......................76,532,352		.03	.04	.08	.25
1913D.....................15,804,000		.35	.55	1.10	2.40
1913S......................6,101,000		1.60	1.75	2.00	3.00
1914.......................75,238,432		.03	.10	.20	.50
1914D*.....................1,193,000		20.00	22.50	30.00	45.00
1914S......................4,137,000		2.00	2.50	3.00	4.50
1915.......................29,092,120		.25	.40	1.25	2.00
1915D.....................22,050,000		.20	.30	.60	1.25
1915S......................4,833,000		1.65	2.00	2.50	3.50
1916......................131,833,677		.02	.03	.06	.20
1916D.....................35,956,000		.05	.10	.40	.75
1916S.....................22,510,000		.15	.25	.50	.90
1917......................196,429,785		.02	.03	.06	.20
1917D.....................55,120,000		.05	.08	.20	.45
1917S.....................32,620,000		.05	.08	.20	.45
1918......................288,104,634		.02	.03	.05	.10
1918D.....................47,830,000		.05	.08	.20	.45
1918S.....................34,680,000		.05	.08	.20	.45
1919......................392,021,000		.02	.03	.05	.10
1919D.....................57,154,000		.03	.05	.10	.25
1919S....................139,760,000		.02	.03	.05	.25
1920......................310,165,000		.02	.03	.05	.10
1920D.....................49,280,000		.04	.06	.10	.25
1920S.....................46,220,000		.04	.06	.10	.25
1921.......................39,157,000		.04	.06	.10	.25
1921S.....................15,274,000		.20	.30	.60	2.00
1922D...................⎫7,160,000		1.15	1.50	1.85	3.00
1922** without D (error)....⎭		16.00	23.50	40.00	58.50
1923.......................74,723,000		.02	.03	.05	.10
1923S......................8,700,000		.40	.65	1.35	2.75
1924.......................75,178,000		.02	.03	.05	.10
1924D......................2,520,000		4.00	5.00	6.75	9.50
1924S.....................11,696,000		.25	.40	.60	1.35
1925......................139,949,000		.02	.03	.05	.10
1925D.....................22,580,000		.05	.10	.20	.35
1925S.....................26,380,000		.05	.10	.20	.35
1926......................157,088,000		.02	.03	.05	.10
1926D.....................28,020,000		.05	.10	.15	.30
1926S......................4,550,000		1.35	1.75	2.35	3.00
1927......................144,440,000		.02	.03	.05	.10
1927D.....................27,170,000		.05	.10	.15	.25
1927S.....................14,276,000		.15	.20	.30	.60
1928......................134,116,000		.02	.03	.05	.10
1928D.....................31,170,000		.03	.04	.05	.10
1928S.....................17,266,000		.04	.06	.10	.20
1929......................185,262,000		.01	.02	.03	.05
1929D.....................41,730,000		.02	.03	.04	.10

*Beware of altered date. No **VDB** on genuine 1914D coin.
**Beware of removed D.

LINCOLN CENTS

	Quan. Minted	Good	V. Good	Fine	V. Fine
1929S	50,148,000	$ .02	$ .03	$ .04	$ .10
1930	157,415,000	.01	.02	.03	.05
1930D	40,100,000	.02	.03	.04	.06
1930S	24,286,000	.03	.04	.05	.10
1931	19,396,000	.06	.08	.12	.20
1931D	4,480,000	1.15	1.35	1.75	2.00
1931S	866,000	12.50	14.00	15.50	17.50
1932	9,062,000	.20	.30	.40	.50
1932D	10,500,000	.15	.25	.35	.45
1933	14,360,000	.15	.25	.35	.45
1933D	6,200,000	.75	.90	1.10	1.35
1934	219,080,000	.01	.01	.01	.03
1934D	28,446,000	.03	.05	.07	.10
1935	245,388,000	.01	.01	.01	.01
1935D	47,000,000	.01	.02	.03	.04
1935S	38,702,000	.02	.03	.04	.05

Proof quantities shown in parentheses

	Quan. Minted	Good	V. Good	Fine	V. Fine
1936 (5,569)	309,637,569	.01	.01	.01	.01
1936D	40,620,000	.01	.02	.03	.04
1936S	29,130,000	.02	.03	.04	.05
1937 (9,320)	309,179,320	.01	.01	.01	.01
1937D	50,430,000	.01	.02	.03	.04
1937S	34,500,000	.02	.03	.04	.05
1938 (14,734)	156,696,734	.01	.01	.01	.01
1938D	20,010,000	.01	.02	.04	.05
1938S	15,180,000	.08	.10	.15	.20
1939 (13,520)	316,479,520	.01	.01	.01	.01
1939D	15,160,000	.08	.10	.15	.20
1939S	52,070,000	.01	.02	.03	.04
1940 (15,872)	586,825,872	.01	.01	.01	.01
1940D	81,390,000	.01	.01	.01	.01
1940S	112,940,000	.01	.01	.01	.01
1941 (21,100)	887,039,100	.01	.01	.01	.01
1941D	128,700,000	.01	.01	.01	.01
1941S	92,360,000	.01	.01	.01	.01
1942 (32,600)	657,828,600	.01	.01	.01	.01
1942D	206,698,000	.01	.01	.01	.01
1942S	85,590,000	.01	.01	.02	.04

Variety 2 — Zinc-coated steel 1943 only

No bronze cents were officially issued in 1943, although a few may have been struck in error. The steel cents of 1943 will be attracted to a magnet while bronze cents will not.

		V. Good	Fine	V. Fine	Ex. F.
1943	684,628,670	.01	.01	.02	.03
1943D	217,660,000	.01	.02	.03	.04
1943S	191,550,000	.02	.03	.05	.10

Variety 1 resumed 1944-1958

		V. Good	Fine	V. Fine	Ex. F.
1944	1,435,400,000	.01	.01	.01	.01
1944D	430,578,000	.01	.01	.01	.01
1944S	282,760,000	.01	.01	.01	.02
1945	1,040,515,000	.01	.01	.01	.01
1945D	226,268,000	.01	.01	.01	.01
1945S	181,770,000	.01	.01	.01	.02

LINCOLN CENTS

	Quan. Minted	V. Fine	Ex. Fine
1946	991,655,000	$ .01	$ .01
1946D	315,690,000	.01	.01
1946S	198,100,000	.01	.02
1947	190,555,000	.01	.01
1947D	194,750,000	.01	.01
1947S	99,000,000	.01	.03
1948	317,570,000	.01	.01
1948D	172,637,500	.01	.01
1948S	81,735,000	.01	.03
1949	217,775,000	.01	.01
1949D	153,132,500	.01	.01
1949S	64,290,000	.02	.04
1950 (51,386)	272,686,386	.01	.01
1950D	334,950,000	.01	.01
1950S	118,505,000	.01	.03
1951 (57,500)	284,633,500	.01	.01
1951D	625,355,000	.01	.01
1951S	136,010,000	.01	.03
1952 (81,980)	186,856,980	.01	.01
1952D	746,130,000	.01	.01
1952S	137,800,004	.01	.02
1953 (128,800)	256,883,800	.01	.01
1953D	700,515,000	.01	.01
1953S	181,835,000	.01	.02
1954 (233,300)	71,873,350	.02	.05
1954D	251,552,500	.01	.01
1954S	96,190,000	.01	.02
1955 (378,200)	330,958,200	.01	.01
1955 "Double die" obverse (error, see picture p. 14)		110.00	140.00
1955D	563,257,500	.01	.01
1955S	44,610,000	.03	.05
1956 (669,384)	421,414,384	.01	.01
1956D	1,098,201,100	.01	.01
1957 (1,247,952)	283,787,952	.01	.01
1957D	1,051,342,000	.01	.01
1958 (875,652)	253,400,652	.01	.01
1958D	800,953,300	.01	.01

LINCOLN MEMORIAL TYPE 1959 to Date

	Quan. Minted	V. Fine	Ex. Fine
1959 (1,149,291)	610,864,291	.01	.01
1959D	1,279,760,000	.01	.01
1960 Large date (Proofs all kinds 1,691,602)	588,096,602	.01	.01
1960 Small date		1.25	1.50
1960D Large date	1,580,884,000	.01	.01
1960D Small date (see picture on page 14)		.01	.01
1961 (3,028,244)	756,373,244	.01	.01
1961D	1,753,266,700	.01	.01
1962 (3,218,019)	609,263,019	.01	.01
1962D	1,793,148,400	.01	.01

LINCOLN CENTS

	Quan. Minted	Ex. Fine		Quan. Minted	Ex. Fine
1963 (3,075,645)	757,185,645	$ .01	1969	1,136,910,000	$.01
1963D	1,774,020,400	.01	1969D	4,002,832,200	.01
1964(3,950,762)	2,652,525,762	.01	1969S (2,934,631)	547,309,631	.01
1964D	3,799,071,500	.01	1970	1,898,315,000	.01
1965	1,497,224,900	.01	1970D	2,891,438,900	.01
1966	2,188,147,783	.01	1970S (2,632,810)	693,192,814	.01
1967	3,048,667,100	.01	1971		.01
1968	1,707,880,970	.01	1971D		.01
1968D	2,886,296,600	.01	1971S		.01
1968S	261,311,510	.01			

"HARD TIMES" AND CIVIL WAR TOKENS

In addition to the coins issued by the United States government, numismatists include in their collection the "Hard Times" and Civil War tokens which circulated as money during two periods in this country's history when nearly all the minor coin was hoarded.

The Hard Times tokens were issued in the period 1834-1844 and are the size of the U.S. cent. They were generally struck in copper in two general groups: political tokens whose theme centered around President Jackson's fight against the United States Bank, and those issued by merchants (tradesmen's cards). Common varieties are worth 50¢ to $1.00 each.

During the Civil War small coin was again hoarded; millions of privately coined tokens of political or advertising nature were placed in circulation. Some 10,000 different varieties have been discovered, most of which are more or less common and worth from 50¢ to $1.00 each. A large majority of the Civil War tokens are about the same size as the present day one-cent piece.

All Cents of 1922 Struck at Denver

An explanation of this variety (without mint mark D) was printed in July, 1964, issue of the *Whitman Numismatic Journal*. Apparently the die from which these coins were struck became worn and the D beneath the date did not appear on several hundred coins that were released for actual circulation.

The number of coins released without the mint mark was very small and therefore they are worth many times the value of those coins with the mint mark showing.

★ ★ ★

The first cent struck at a branch mint was in 1908, the San Francisco Indian Head Cent.

Beware of altered dates on 1914D Cents. There are no designer's initials VDB on genuine specimens. See details page 13.

★ ★ ★

E Pluribus Unum (One composed of many) is the most familiar legend to be found on U.S. Coins. Its equivalent, but with different wording, appeared on money issued prior to the establishment of the mint. Here are a few: A 1776 New York note, "Uno Eodemque Igne" (One and the same fire). One of the Continental notes pictures a harp with 13 strings accompanied by this motto, "Majora Minoribua Consonant" (The greater and the smaller ones sound together). On another note is a circled chain of 13 links and the motto, "We are one."

TWO-CENT BRONZE
Issued from 1864 through 1873

Those of 1864 are of two varieties: small letters in the motto, "In God We Trust," and the second variety has the same letters in a slightly larger size. Those of the large motto variety are the commonest of the two-cent pieces, while the small motto is the rarest. It is a little difficult to distinguish the two sizes of mottos without some study. The D in GOD is wide in proportion to its height on the small motto variety (see page 13). The two-cent piece was the first United States coin to bear the motto, "In God We Trust."

GOOD—At least IN GOD visible.
V. GOOD—WE weakly visible.
FINE—Complete Motto visible. WE weak.
EX. FINE—WE is bold.

	Quan. Minted	Good	V. Good	Fine	Ex. Fine
1864 Small motto	} 19,847,500	$23.50	$32.50	$40.00	$60.00
Large motto		1.15	1.50	2.00	4.50
1865	13,640,000	1.15	1.50	2.00	4.50
1866	3,177,000	1.25	1.75	2.75	6.00
1867	2,938,750	1.25	1.75	2.75	6.00
1868	2,803,750	1.25	1.75	2.75	6.00
1869	1,546,500	1.75	2.50	3.75	7.00
1870	861,250	2.50	3.25	5.00	9.00
1871	721,250	2.75	3.75	6.50	12.50
1872	65,000	21.00	23.50	34.00	47.50
					Proof
1873 Proofs only					385.00

NICKEL THREE-CENT PIECES
Issued from 1865 through 1889

This coinage was authorized for the purpose of retiring the 3-cent fractional currency notes. All dates are of the same type. The two rarest dates are 1877 and 1878, both of which were struck in proof only. A variety of 1887 has the date engraved over an "86."

GOOD—Date and legends complete though worn. III smooth.
V. GOOD—III is half worn. Rims complete.
FINE—Hair curls well defined.
EX. FINE—Slight, even wear.

	Quan. Minted	Good	V. Good	Fine	Ex. Fine
1865	11,382,000	1.15	1.50	1.70	2.75
1866	4,801,000	1.15	1.50	1.70	2.75
1867	3,915,000	1.15	1.50	1.70	2.75
1868	3,252,000	1.15	1.50	1.70	2.75
1869	1,604,000	1.25	1.60	2.00	3.00

NICKEL THREE-CENT PIECES

	Quan. Minted	Good	V. Good	Fine	Ex. Fine	Proof
1870	1,335,000	$1.25	$1.60	$2.00	$3.25	
1871	604,000	1.60	2.00	3.00	5.25	
1872	862,000	1.60	2.00	3.00	5.25	
1873	1,173,000	1.25	1.60	2.00	3.25	
1874	790,000	1.60	2.00	3.00	5.25	
1875	228,000	2.60	3.35	4.50	10.50	
1876	162,000	2.60	3.35	4.50	10.50	
1877 Proofs only						$435.00
1878 Proofs only	2,350					120.00
1879	41,200	4.00	4.50	5.50	8.00	40.00
1880	24,955	4.00	5.50	7.00	9.00	40.00
1881	1,080,575	1.30	1.50	2.00	3.25	30.00
1882	25,300	4.00	5.00	6.00	8.50	30.00
1883	10,609	4.00	5.00	6.00	8.50	30.00
1884	5,642	5.00	6.00	7.75	12.00	40.00
1885	4,790	5.00	6.00	7.75	12.00	42.50
1886 Proofs only	4,290					45.00
1887 7 over 6 (Proofs only)						140.00
1887 Normal date	7,961	10.00	12.50	15.00	22.50	90.00
1888	41,083	4.00	5.00	6.00	8.75	35.00
1889	21,561	4.00	5.00	6.00	8.75	35.00

FIVE-CENT NICKELS

Issued from 1866 to date

Authorized for the purpose of retiring fractional currency notes of the denomination of less than 10 cents.

The first type is known as the "shield type" and has two varieties; both 1866 and 1867 have rays through the stars (1867 also was coined without the rays). Proofs only were coined for the years 1877 and 1878, the former being the rarest date of the shield type and also of the entire 5 cent nickel series, except 1913.

In 1883 the type was changed to the more or less familiar "Liberty head." This type first appeared without the word "cents" on the coin; merely a large letter "V" to denote denomination. As this coin is about the size of a five-dollar gold piece these "cent-less" nickels were immediately gold-plated and passed on unsuspecting people for five dollars. Later in the year the word "cents" was added. The cent-less variety was hoarded in great numbers and frequently turns up today. 1885 and 1912S mint are the rarest dates of this type.

The 1913 Liberty Head Nickel did not become known to the numismatic world until 1920, when five specimens were exhibited at a meeting of coin collectors in Chicago. Very clever fake 1913's have been made by altering 1903 and 1910 nickels.

Indian Head type nickels were first coined in 1913 with the buffalo or "bison" standing on "raised" ground. This is known as Variety 1; the ground or plane was recessed to form Variety 2.

In 1938 the Treasury of the United States announced a public competition for a new design, it being specified that the head of Jefferson and a reproduction of his home, Monticello, be the important features. Some 390 entries were received and Felix Schlag of Chicago won the $1,000 prize.

FIVE-CENT NICKELS

SHIELD TYPE 1866-1883

Rays between stars 1866-1867   Without Rays 1867-1883

GOOD—*All letters in Motto readable.*
V. GOOD—*Motto stands out clearly. Rims worn slightly but even. Part of shield lines visible.*
FINE—*Half of each olive leaf is smooth.*
EX. FINE—*Leaf tips show slight wear. Cross over shield slightly worn.*

	Quan. Minted	Good	V. Good	Fine	Ex. Fine
1866 Rays through stars	14,742,500	$3.00	$3.50	$6.00	$16.50
1867 Rays	⎫ 30,909,500	4.00	6.00	12.00	25.00
Without Rays	⎭	1.35	1.75	2.10	4.75
1868	28,817,000	1.35	1.75	2.10	4.75
1869	16,395,000	1.50	2.00	2.85	6.00
1870	4,806,000	2.00	2.75	4.00	8.00
1871	561,000	16.00	21.00	32.50	50.00
1872	6,036,000	2.25	3.00	4.25	8.50
1873	4,550,000	2.00	2.75	4.00	8.00
1874	3,538,000	3.00	3.50	5.50	10.00
1875	2,097,000	6.50	7.50	11.50	25.00
1876	2,530,000	3.50	4.00	6.00	11.50
1877 Proofs only	estimated 500			Proof	585.00
1878 Proofs only	2,350			Proof	125.00
1879	29,100	8.00	9.50	12.50	22.50
1880	19,955	11.00	13.50	17.50	25.00
1881	72,375	7.50	9.00	12.00	18.50
1882	11,476,600	1.35	1.75	2.25	5.00
1883 Shield type	1,456,919	1.50	2.25	3.00	5.75

LIBERTY HEAD TYPE 1883-1913

Without CENTS 1883   With CENTS 1883-1912

GOOD—*No detail in head. LIBERTY obliterated.*
V. GOOD—*At least 3 letters in LIBERTY readable.*
FINE—*All letters in LIBERTY show.*
EX. FINE—*LIBERTY sharp. Corn grains at bottom of wreath show, on reverse.*

FIVE-CENT NICKELS

	Quan. Minted	Good	V. Good	Fine	Ex. Fine
1883 Liberty, without CENTS	5,479,519	$ .35	$ .55	$ .75	$1.75
1883 Liberty, with CENTS	16,032,983	2.00	2.85	4.65	8.00
1884	11,273,942	2.00	3.00	5.00	8.75
1885	1,476,490	30.00	40.00	55.00	82.50
1886	3,330,290	15.00	18.00	27.50	42.00
1887	15,263,652	1.25	1.50	2.65	5.50
1888	10,720,483	2.25	3.00	5.00	9.50
1889	15,881,361	1.25	1.60	2.75	5.00
1890	16,259,272	1.50	2.00	3.25	6.75
1891	16,834,350	1.10	1.50	2.25	5.00
1892	11,699,642	1.25	1.85	2.90	5.50
1893	13,370,195	1.10	1.50	2.25	5.00
1894	5,413,132	2.25	3.00	5.00	9.50
1895	9,979,884	.90	1.30	2.25	4.75
1896	8,842,920	1.00	1.50	3.50	9.50
1897	20,428,735	.25	.40	1.00	3.50
1898	12,532,087	.25	.40	1.00	3.50
1899	26,029,031	.25	.40	.75	3.25
1900	27,255,995	.12	.20	.35	1.25
1901	26,480,213	.12	.20	.35	1.25
1902	31,480,579	.12	.20	.35	1.25
1903	28,006,725	.12	.20	.35	1.25
1904	21,404,984	.12	.20	.35	1.25
1905	29,827,276	.12	.20	.35	1.25
1906	38,613,725	.12	.20	.35	1.25
1907	39,214,800	.12	.20	.35	1.25
1908	22,686,177	.12	.20	.35	1.25
1909	11,590,526	.25	.45	.60	2.25
1910	30,169,353	.12	.20	.35	1.25
1911	39,559,372	.12	.20	.35	1.25
1912	26,236,714	.12	.20	.35	1.25
1912D	8,474,000	.30	.60	1.50	17.00
1912S	238,000	15.00	18.00	26.00	60.00

1913 Liberty Head (not a regular issue, beware altered date). ———

James E. Fraser, who designed the Buffalo Nickel, used three different Indians to obtain the portrait on the obverse side. The models were Iron Tail, a Sioux warrior; Two Moons, a Cheyenne chief; and John Big Tree, an Onondaga chief. The bison was modeled after "Black Diamond" in the New York Zoological Garden. The famous animal was slaughtered in 1915 and his massive head was preserved and mounted.

Variety 1	Variety 2
Bison on mound	Bison on plane

GOOD—*Legends and date readable. Horn worn off.*
V. GOOD—*Half horn shows.*
FINE—*Two-thirds horn shows. Obv. rim intact.*
EX. FINE—*Full horn. Slight wear on Indian's hair ribbon.*

FIVE-CENT NICKELS

	Quan. Minted	Good	V. Good	Fine	Ex. Fine
1913 Indian head — Variety 1 —					
Bison on mound........30,993,520	$ .35	$ .50	$ .90	$1.25
1913D Variety 1 5,337,000	1.25	1.85	2.50	4.50
1913S Variety 1..............2,105,000	2.75	3.50	4.25	8.25
1913 Indian head — Variety 2 —					
Bison on plane.........29,858,700	.70	1.00	1.45	2.00
1913D Variety 2..............4,156,000	8.00	11.00	13.50	19.00
1913S Variety 2..............1,209,000	16.25	21.50	26.00	37.50
1914......................20,665,738	.60	.85	1.25	3.00
1914D......................3,912,000	8.25	10.00	14.50	22.50
1914S......................3,470,000	1.50	2.50	4.25	11.00
1915......................20,987,270	.40	.65	1.25	2.50
1915D......................7,569,500	1.50	2.50	4.25	12.00
1915S......................1,505,000	3.25	4.50	7.00	19.00
1916......................63,498,066	.15	.25	.60	2.00
1916D.....................13,333,000	1.00	1.75	2.75	8.00
1916S.....................11,860,000	.85	1.40	2.75	9.50
1917......................51,424,029	.15	.25	.60	2.00
1917D......................9,910,800	1.15	1.75	4.00	17.50
1917S......................4,193,000	1.35	2.00	4.25	17.50
1918......................32,086,314	.15	.25	.60	2.00
1918D 8 over 7 ....⎱8,362,000	90.00	130.00	235.00	625.00
Normal date ....⎰	1.15	2.25	4.25	22.00
1918S......................4,882,000	1.00	1.90	4.25	20.00
1919......................60,868,000	.15	.25	.60	1.75
1919D......................8,006,000	1.25	2.25	5.50	32.50
1919S......................7,521,000	1.25	2.25	5.50	32.50
1920......................63,093,000	.12	.20	.40	1.50
1920D......................9,418,000	1.00	1.75	4.00	25.00
1920S......................9,689,000	.75	1.50	3.50	24.00
1921......................10,663,000	.15	.25	.75	3.75
1921S......................1,557,000	4.00	6.75	11.00	42.50
1923......................35,715,000	.12	.20	.40	1.50
1923S......................6,142,000	.60	1.35	3.00	20.00
1924......................21,620,000	.12	.20	.40	1.50
1924D......................5,258,000	.75	1.10	2.75	22.00
1924S......................1,437,000	2.00	3.25	8.00	50.00
1925......................35,565,100	.12	.20	.40	1.50
1925D......................4,450,000	1.50	3.00	5.50	20.00
1925S......................6,256,000	1.25	2.50	5.00	22.00
1926......................44,693,000	.07	.12	.20	1.25
1926D......................5,638,000	1.00	1.75	3.00	22.00
1926S........................970,000	2.25	4.00	7.50	60.00
1927......................37,981,000	.07	.12	.20	1.00
1927D......................5,730,000	.30	.65	1.50	5.50
1927S......................3,430,000	.50	1.00	2.75	23.00
1928......................23,411,000	.07	.12	.20	.75
1928D......................6,436,000	.10	.20	.35	1.25
1928S......................6,936,000	.15	.25	.45	3.50
1929......................36,446,000	.07	.12	.20	.75
1929D......................8,370,000	.10	.20	.35	1.25
1929S......................7,754,000	.10	.20	.35	1.25
1930......................22,849,000	.07	.12	.20	.60
1930S......................5,435,000	.15	.30	.60	1.75

FIVE-CENT NICKELS

	Quan. Minted	Good	V. Good	Fine	Ex. Fine
1931S	1,200,000	$1.50	$2.00	$2.75	$6.00
1934	20,213,003	.07	.10	.20	.50
1934D	7,480,000	.10	.15	.25	.50
1935	58,264,000	.05	.08	.10	.25
1935D	12,092,000	.05	.08	.10	.25
1935S	10,300,000	.05	.08	.10	.25
1936 (Proofs 4,420)	119,001,420	.05	.08	.10	.20
1936D	24,814,000	.05	.08	.10	.20
1936S	14,930,000	.05	.08	.10	.20
1937 (Proofs 5,769)	79,485,769	.05	.08	.10	.20
1937D Normal	⎫ 17,826,000	.05	.08	.10	.20
1937D* Three-legged Buffalo	⎭	17.50	21.00	26.00	42.00
1937S	5,635,000	.10	.15	.20	.35
1938D Buffalo — All kinds	7,020,000	.05	.08	.15	.30
1938D over S (See illustration page 14).				2.50	5.00

*Beware of alterations (removed leg).

JEFFERSON TYPE 1938 to Date

VERY GOOD—Second porch pillar from right nearly gone, other three still visible but weak.
EX. FINE—Cheekbone, hairlines, eyebrow slightly worn but well defined. Base of triangle above pillars visible but weak.

	Quan. Minted	Very Good	Ex. Fine		Quan. Minted	Very Good	Ex. Fine
1938 (Proofs 19,365)				1940D	43,540,000	$ .05	$ .05
Jefferson	19,515,365	$ .07	$ .20	1940S	39,690,000	.05	.10
1938D	5,376,000	.50	1.00	1941 (Proofs 18,720)			
1938S	4,105,000	1.00	2.10		203,283,720	.05	.05
1939 (Proofs 12,535)				1941D	53,432,000	.05	.10
	120,627,535	.05	.05	1941S	43,445,000	.05	.10
1939D	3,514,000	1.75	4.25	1942 (Proofs 29,600)			
1939S	6,630,000	.30	1.10		49,818,600	.05	.05
1940 (Proofs 14,158)				1942D	13,938,000	.10	.35
	176,499,158	.05	.05				

WARTIME SILVER FIVE-CENT PIECES

(Mint mark above dome on reverse side)

All nickels before 1956 have a premium in bright uncirculated condition.

	Quan. Minted	Very Good	Ex. Fine		Quan. Minted	Very Good	Ex. Fine
1942P (Proofs 27,600)				1944P	119,150,000	$ .10	$ .20
	57,900,600	$ .10	$ .25	1944D	32,309,000	.10	.25
1942S	32,900,000	.10	.25	1944S	21,640,000	.10	.35
1943P	271,165,000	.10	.20	1945P	119,408,100	.10	.25
1943D	15,294,000	.20	.80	1945D	37,158,000	.10	.35
1943S	104,060,000	.10	.20	1945S	58,939,000	.10	.30

FIVE-CENT NICKELS
PREWAR COPPER-NICKEL COMPOSITION RESUMED

	Quan. Minted	Ex. Fine		Quan. Minted	Ex. Fine
1946	161,116,000	$ .05	1956D	67,222,940	$ .05
1946D	45,292,200	.05	1957 (1,247,952)	39,655,952	.05
1946S	13,560,000	.15	1957D	136,828,900	.05
1947	95,000,000	.05	1958 (875,652)	17,963,652	.10
1947D	37,822,000	.05	1958D	168,249,120	.05
1947S	24,720,000	.10	1959 (1,149,291)	28,397,291	.05
1948	89,348,000	.05	1959D	160,738,240	.05
1948D	44,734,000	.08	1960 (1,691,602)	57,107,602	.05
1948S	11,300,000	.15	1960D	192,582,180	.05
1949	60,652,000	.05	1961 (3,028,244)	76,668,244	.05
1949D	36,498,000	.05	1961D	229,342,760	.05
1949S	9,716,000	.25	1962 (3,218,019)	100,602,019	.05
1950 (51,386)	9,847,386	.20	1962D	280,195,720	.05
1950D	2,630,030	5.00	1963 (3,075,645)	178,851,645	.05
1951 (57,500)	28,609,500	.05	1963D	276,829,460	.05
1951D	20,460,000	.05	1964(3,950,762)	1,028,622,762	.05
1951S	7,776,000	.45	1964D	1,787,297,160	.05
1952 (81,980)	64,069,980	.05	1965	136,131,380	.05
1952D	30,638,000	.08	1966	156,208,283	.05
1952S	20,572,000	.08	1967	107,325,800	.05
1953 (128,800)	46,772,800	.05	1968D	91,227,880	.05
1953D	59,878,600	.05	1968S	103,437,510	.05
1953S	19,210,900	.08	1969D	202,807,500	.05
1954 (233,300)	47,917,350	.05	1969S (2,934,631)	123,099,631	.05
1954D	117,183,060	.05	1970D	515,485,380	.05
1954S	29,384,000	.05	1970S (2,632,810)	241,464,814	.05
1955 (378,200)	8,266,200	.30	1971		.05
1955D	74,464,100	.05	1971D		.05
1956 (669,384)	35,885,384	.05	1971S Proof only		1.50

SILVER THREE-CENT PIECES
Issued from 1851 through 1873

Authorized to facilitate postal transactions; however, due to its small size it became unpopular.

The same general design was used throughout the entire coinage except for some minor changes in design and alloy. In 1854 the size of the star on the obverse was enlarged as was the size of the date, and arrows and branches were added. In 1859 the outlines on the star were reduced from three to two and the size of the date was reduced. Those bearing the date 1864 are the rarest of the series.

GOOD—*Star worn smooth. Legend and date readable.*
V. GOOD—*Outline of shield defined. Legend and date clear.*
FINE—*Only star points worn smooth.*
V. FINE—*Only partial wear on star ridges.*

SILVER THREE-CENT PIECES

	Quan. Minted	Good	V. Good	Fine	V. Fine
Variety 1: No outline around star					
1851.....................5,447,400	$2.25	$3.25	$4.25	$8.00
1851O.....................720,000	5.50	8.00	13.50	25.00
1852.....................18,663,500	1.80	2.50	4.25	8.00
1853.....................11,400,000	1.80	2.50	4.25	8.00
Variety 2: Three outlines to star, large date					
1854.....................671,000	4.00	5.00	7.50	12.50
1855.....................139,000	7.00	10.00	17.00	30.00
1856.....................1,458,000	3.50	5.00	7.50	12.50
1857.....................1,042,000	3.50	5.00	7.50	12.50
1858.....................1,604,000	3.25	4.50	6.00	12.00
Variety 3: Two outlines to star, small date					
1859.....................365,000	5.75	6.50	8.00	13.00
1860.....................287,000	5.75	6.50	8.00	13.00
1861.....................498,000	3.50	4.50	7.50	11.00
1862.....................343,550	3.50	4.50	7.50	11.00

		Unc.	Proof
1863.....................21,460	....	$100.00	$140.00
1864.....................12,470	....	135.00	165.00
1865.....................8,500			150.00
1866.....................22,725			85.00
1867.....................4,625			85.00
1868.....................4,100			85.00
1869.....................5,100			85.00
1870.....................4,000			85.00
1871.....................4,360			85.00
1872.....................1,950			85.00
1873 Proofs only.....................600			160.00

HALF DIMES

Issued from 1794 through 1873

Coinage for general circulation started with 1794 although some believe the 1792 half disme to be a regular issue (see page 5). All the early dates, those before 1829, are more or less rare, with the 1802 being one of the great United States silver rarities.

Die varieties are numerous in this series; one curious variety is that of the year 1800 where the word "Liberty" is spelled "LIBEKTY."

Abbreviations used in describing half dimes (those not previously explained in preceding pages) are:

Ars. — arrows. (Arrows at the date on 1853, 1854 and 1855.)

Drap. — drapery. (Drapery on the left elbow of Liberty.)

	Quan. Minted	Fair	Good	V. Good	Fine	V. Fine
1792 Half Disme..............		$200.00	$300.00	$375.00	$500.00	$750.00

HALF DIMES
FLOWING HAIR TYPE 1794-1795

FAIR—*Details clear enough to identify.*

GOOD—*Eagle, wreath, bust outlined but lack details.*

V. GOOD—*Some details remain on face. All lettering readable.*

FINE—*Hair ends show. Hair at top smooth.*

V. FINE—*Hairlines at top show. Hair about ear defined.*

	Quan. Minted	Fair	Good	V. Good	Fine	V. Fine
1794	} 86,416	$55.00	$110.00	$180.00	$260.00	$425.00
1795		45.00	90.00	125.00	185.00	285.00

DRAPED BUST TYPE, SMALL EAGLE REVERSE 1796-1797

FAIR—*Details clear enough to identify.*

GOOD—*Date, stars, LIBERTY readable. Bust outlined but no details.*

V. GOOD—*Some details show.*

FINE—*Hair and drapery lines worn, but visible.*

V. FINE—*Only left of drapery indistinct.*

1796	10,230	55.00	100.00	165.00	225.00	325.00
1797 15 stars	} 44,527	45.00	90.00	135.00	190.00	275.00
16 stars		45.00	90.00	135.00	190.00	275.00
13 stars		45.00	90.00	135.00	190.00	275.00

DRAPED BUST TYPE, HERALDIC EAGLE REVERSE 1800-1805

1800 Normal obv.	} 24,000	42.50	75.00	110.00	160.00	265.00
LIBEKTY var.		42.50	75.00	110.00	160.00	265.00
1801	33,910	45.00	80.00	120.00	175.00	275.00
1802 (Rare)	13,010	345.00	745.00	1200.00	1700.00	2650.00
1803	37,850	37.50	65.00	100.00	145.00	215.00
1805	15,600	57.50	95.00	150.00	250.00	375.00

CAPPED BUST TYPE 1829-1837

GOOD—*Bust outlined, no detail. Date and legend readable.*

V. GOOD—*Complete legend and date plain. At least 3 letters of LIBERTY show clearly.*

FINE—*All letters in LIBERTY show.*

V. FINE—*Full rim, both sides. Clasp on shoulder and ear well defined.*

	Quan. Minted	Good	V. Good	Fine	V. Fine
1829	1,230,000	3.75	4.00	5.50	12.50
1830	1,240,000	3.50	4.00	5.50	11.00
1831	1,242,700	3.50	4.00	5.50	11.00
1832	965,000	3.50	4.00	5.50	11.00
1833	1,370,000	3.50	4.00	5.50	11.00
1834	1,480,000	3.50	4.00	5.50	11.00
1835	2,760,000	3.50	4.00	5.50	11.00
1836	1,900,000	3.50	4.00	5.50	11.00
1837	both types 2,276,000	3.50	4.00	5.50	11.00

HALF DIMES
LIBERTY SEATED TYPE 1837-1873
Variety 1 — No stars on obverse 1837-1838

GOOD—*LIBERTY on shield smooth. Date and letters readable.*
V. GOOD—*At least 3 letters in LIBERTY are visible.*
FINE—*Entire LIBERTY visible, weak spots.*
V. FINE—*Entire LIBERTY strong and even.*

	Quan. Minted	Good	V. Good	Fine	V. Fine
1837 No stars...............	inc. above	$20.00	$27.50	$37.50	$50.00
1838O No stars...............	70,000	25.00	35.00	45.00	80.00

Variety 2 — Stars on obverse 1838-1859

1838 With stars.............	2,255,000	1.50	2.00	3.00	6.00
1839.......................	1,069,150	1.50	2.00	3.00	6.00
1839O......................	1,034,039	2.50	3.00	5.00	9.00
1840.......................	1,344,085	1.35	1.75	2.75	5.00
1840O......................	935,000	2.50	3.75	6.25	13.00
1841.......................	1,150,000	1.35	1.75	2.50	4.50
1841O......................	815,000	1.75	2.75	4.50	8.00
1842.......................	815,000	1.50	2.00	2.50	4.50
1842O......................	350,000	2.75	5.00	8.50	16.00
1843.......................	1,165,000	1.35	1.75	2.50	4.50
1844.......................	430,000	1.75	2.75	4.25	6.00
1844O......................	220,000	3.25	5.50	9.50	18.00
1845.......................	1,564,000	1.35	1.75	2.50	4.00
1846.......................	27,000	23.50	32.50	45.00	60.00
1847.......................	1,274,000	1.35	1.75	2.50	4.00
1848.......................	668,000	1.35	1.75	2.50	4.00
1848O......................	600,000	2.50	3.75	6.25	13.00
1849.......................	1,309,000	1.35	1.75	2.25	4.00
1849O......................	140,000	12.50	20.00	30.00	47.00
1850.......................	955,000	1.35	1.75	2.25	4.00
1850O......................	690,000	1.75	2.75	4.25	10.00
1851.......................	781,000	1.35	1.75	2.25	4.00
1851O......................	860,000	1.50	2.50	4.00	9.00
1852.......................	1,000,500	1.35	1.75	2.25	4.00
1852O......................	260,000	2.50	4.00	7.50	16.00
1853 No arrows.............	135,000	4.00	6.00	10.00	16.00
1853O No arrows.............	160,000	30.00	40.00	60.00	85.00

Variety 3 — Arrows at date 1853-1855

Arrows at either side of date were added to indicate reduction of weight.
Genuine specimens without arrows should weigh more than specimens with
arrows.

1853 With arrows...........	13,210,020	1.50	2.00	2.50	5.00
1853O With arrows...........	2,200,000	1.50	2.00	2.50	5.00
1854 Arrows................	5,740,000	1.35	1.75	2.00	3.00
1854O Arrows...............	1,560,000	1.35	1.75	2.25	4.00
1855 Arrows................	1,750,000	1.35	1.75	2.00	3.00
1855O Arrows...............	600,000	1.75	2.50	4.00	9.00

HALF DIMES
Variety 2 resumed 1856-1859

	Quan. Minted	Good	V. Good	Fine	V. Fine
1856 No arrows	4,880,000	$1.35	$1.75	$2.00	$2.50
1856O	1,100,000	1.35	1.75	2.50	4.00
1857	7,280,000	1.35	1.75	2.00	2.50
1857O	1,380,000	1.35	1.75	2.25	4.00
1858	3,500,000	1.35	1.75	2.00	2.50
1858O	1,660,000	1.35	1.75	2.25	4.00
1859	340,000	1.75	2.50	3.50	5.00
1859O	560,000	1.50	2.00	3.00	4.50

In the years 1859 and 1860 a half-dime type was struck which does not bear our nation's identity. These coins are known as transitional patterns, and were struck at the time the inscription UNITED STATES OF AMERICA was being transferred from the reverse to the obverse side of the coin. These coins are not a regular mint issue.

1859 (Obv. of 1859. Rev. of 1860)......	Proof $1000.00
1860 Stars	
(Obv. of 1859. Rev. of 1860)...100	Unc. 500.00

Variety 4 — Legend on obverse 1860-1873

1860 Legend	799,000	1.35	1.75	2.00	2.75
1860O Legend	1,060,000	1.50	2.25	3.00	4.50
1861	3,361,000	1.35	1.75	2.00	2.50
1862	1,492,550	1.35	1.75	2.00	2.50
1863	18,460	5.00	6.00	8.00	14.00
1863S	100,000	5.00	6.00	8.00	15.00
1864	48,470			Proof	175.00
1864S	90,000	5.00	7.50	12.50	20.00
1865	13,500	5.00	7.50	9.00	15.00
1865S	120,000	3.50	5.00	7.50	12.50
1866	10,725	3.50	5.00	7.50	12.50
1866S	120,000	2.50	4.00	6.50	10.50
1867	8,625	3.50	5.00	7.50	12.50
1867S	120,000	2.50	3.50	5.00	11.00
1868	89,200	1.75	2.50	3.50	6.00
1868S	280,000	1.50	2.25	3.50	6.00
1869	208,600	1.50	2.25	3.00	4.50
1869S	230,000	1.50	2.25	3.50	6.00
1870	536,600	1.35	1.75	2.00	2.50
1871	1,873,960	1.35	1.75	2.00	2.50
1871S	161,000	4.50	7.00	10.00	16.00
1872	2,947,950	1.35	1.75	2.00	2.50
1872S Mint mark within wreath }	837,000	1.40	2.00	2.50	4.00
Mint mark below wreath . }		1.50	2.25	2.65	4.50
1873	712,600	1.35	1.75	1.75	2.50
1873S	324,000	1.35	1.75	2.50	5.00

DIMES
Issued from 1796 to date

The designs of the dimes follow very closely those of the half dime up through the Liberty seated type Also, in similar fashion to half dime, there is nothing in the design of the early dates to indicate the value of the piece. The early dates are scarce, especially in choice condition.

The Liberty head type issued from 1892 to 1916 is erroneously called "Morgan Type." The design was by Barber, and each coin has his initial **B** on the truncation of the neck.

DRAPED BUST TYPE, SMALL EAGLE REVERSE 1796-1797

FAIR—*Details clear enough to identify.*
GOOD—*Date readable. Bust outlined, but no detail.*
V. GOOD—*All but deepest drapery folds worn smooth. Hairlines nearly gone and curls lack detail.*
FINE—*All drapery lines visible. Hair partly worn.*
V. FINE—*Only left side of drapery is indistinct.*

	Quan. Minted	Fair	Good	V. Good	Fine	V. Fine
1796...................	22,135	$100.00	$175.00	$250.00	$410.00	$625.00
1797 16 stars..........	} 25,261	85.00	165.00	215.00	375.00	500.00
13 stars..........		75.00	150.00	200.00	325.00	475.00

DRAPED BUST TYPE, HERALDIC EAGLE REVERSE 1798-1807

1798 All kinds.......... 27,550					
8 over 7, 16 stars on Rev .	35.00	60.00	85.00	140.00	235.00
8 over 7, 13 stars on Rev .				250.00	550.00
Normal date............	35.00	60.00	85.00	140.00	235.00
1800.................21,760	32.50	50.00	75.00	110.00	185.00
1801.................34,640	37.50	60.00	95.00	150.00	240.00
1802.................10,975	40.00	65.00	100.00	160.00	250.00
1803.................33,040	37.50	60.00	95.00	150.00	240.00
1804..................8,265	50.00	80.00	105.00	180.00	300.00
1805................120,780	25.00	45.00	55.00	77.50	140.00
1807................165,000	25.00	45.00	55.00	75.00	135.00

CAPPED BUST TYPE 1809-1837
Variety 1 — Large size 1809-1828

GOOD—*Date, letters and stars discernible. Bust outlined, no details.*
V. GOOD—*Legends and date plain. Minimum of 3 letters in LIBERTY show.*
FINE—*Full LIBERTY. Ear and shoulder clasp visible. Part of rim shows on both sides.*
V. FINE—*LIBERTY distinct. Full rim. Ear and clasp plain and distinct.*

DIMES

	Quan. Minted	Good	V. Good	Fine	V. Fine
1809	44,710	$25.00	$37.50	$50.00	$ 80.00
1811 11 over 09	65,180	17.50	21.00	31.50	45.00
1814	421,500	7.00	9.00	12.50	21.00
1820	942,587	4.50	6.00	8.50	16.50
1821	1,186,512	4.50	6.00	8.50	16.50
1822	100,000	22.50	30.00	50.00	100.00
1823	440,000	5.00	7.00	12.00	25.00
1824 4 over 2		7.00	9.00	15.00	25.00
1825	510,000	4.50	6.00	9.50	15.00
1827	1,215,000	3.50	5.00	7.50	15.00
1828 Large Date	}125,000	11.00	16.00	26.00	45.00
Small Date		6.50	8.50	12.50	26.00

Variety 2 — Reduced size 1829-1837

		Good	V. Good	Fine	V. Fine
1829 Small and medium 10c	}770,000	3.00	4.00	7.00	11.00
Large 10c		5.00	8.00	14.00	20.00
1830	510,000	2.25	3.50	4.75	8.00
1831	771,350	2.25	3.50	4.75	8.00
1832	522,500	2.25	3.50	4.75	8.00
1833	485,000	2.25	3.50	4.75	8.00
1834	635,000	2.25	3.50	4.75	8.00
1835	1,410,000	2.25	3.50	4.75	8.00
1836	1,190,000	2.25	3.50	4.75	8.00
1837 both types	1,042,000	2.25	3.50	4.75	8.00

LIBERTY SEATED TYPE 1837-1891

GOOD—*LIBERTY on shield smooth. Date and letters readable.*

V. GOOD—*At least 3 letters in LIBERTY are visible.*

FINE—*Entire LIBERTY visible, weak spots.*

V. FINE—*Entire LIBERTY strong and even.*

1837 Liberty seated, no stars		20.00	30.00	45.00	75.00
1838O Liberty seated, no stars	406,034	25.00	37.50	65.00	110.00

Stars on
Obverse
1838-1860

1838	1,992,500	2.50	3.00	3.75	6.00
1839	1,053,115	1.50	2.00	3.00	5.50
1839O	1,323,000	2.25	3.50	5.50	8.50
1840	1,358,580	1.50	2.25	3.50	6.00

DIMES

	Quan. Minted	Good	V. Good	Fine	V. Fine
1840O No drapery	1,175,000	$2.25	$3.50	$5.25	$8.00
1841 No drapery	} 1,622,500				
1841 Drapery		1.00	1.75	2.50	4.75
1841O	2,007,500	1.00	1.75	3.00	6.00
1842	1,887,500	1.00	1.50	2.25	4.50
1842O	2,020,000	2.00	3.00	4.00	8.00
1843	1,370,000	1.00	1.50	2.25	4.50
1843O	150,000	6.00	9.00	15.00	25.00
1844	72,500	10.00	16.00	26.00	40.00
1845	1,755,000	1.00	1.50	2.25	4.50
1845O	230,000	3.50	5.00	7.00	12.00
1846	31,300	6.50	8.00	13.00	21.00
1847	245,000	2.25	3.00	4.50	8.50
1848	451,500	1.75	2.50	3.50	6.00
1849	839,000	1.00	1.50	2.25	4.50
1849O	300,000	3.00	4.25	7.50	14.00
1850	1,931,500	1.00	1.50	2.25	4.50
1850O	510,000	2.50	4.00	6.00	11.00
1851	1,026,500	1.00	1.50	2.25	4.50
1851O	400,000	2.00	3.00	4.25	8.00
1852	1,535,500	1.00	1.50	2.25	4.50
1852O	430,000	2.25	3.25	5.00	10.00
1853 No arrows at date	95,000	7.00	10.00	13.00	21.00
1853 With arrows	12,078,010	1.25	1.75	2.50	5.00
1853O (Arrows)	1,100,000	2.00	2.75	3.50	6.00
1854 (Arrows)	4,470,000	1.25	1.75	2.25	4.50
1854O (Arrows)	1,770,000	1.25	1.75	2.50	5.00
1855 (Arrows)	2,075,000	1.25	1.75	2.25	4.50
1856	5,780,000	1.25	1.75	2.50	4.50
1856O	1,180,000	1.50	2.00	3.00	5.00
1856S	70,000	12.50	20.00	30.00	50.00
1857	5,580,000	1.00	1.50	2.00	3.50
1857O	1,540,000	1.25	1.75	2.50	5.00
1858	1,540,000	1.00	1.50	2.00	3.50
1858O	290,000	2.00	3.00	4.00	7.50
1858S	60,000	8.00	12.00	18.00	37.00
1859	430,000	1.00	1.50	2.25	3.75
1859 Obv. of 1859. Rev. of 1860					
1859O	480,000	1.00	1.50	2.25	5.00
1859S	60,000	8.00	11.00	16.00	27.50
1860S (Stars on Obv.)	140,000	4.00	6.00	11.00	20.00

Legend on
Obverse
1860-1891

1860 (Legend replaces stars)	607,000	1.00	1.50	2.25	4.00
1860O	40,000	32.50	50.00	75.00	125.00
1861	1,884,000	.85	1.35	1.75	3.00
1861S	172,500	6.00	9.00	15.00	25.00
1862	847,550	1.20	1.50	2.25	4.00

DIMES

	Quan. Minted	Good	V. Good	Fine	V. Fine
1862S	180,750	$ 4.00	$ 6.50	$11.00	$22.50
1863	14,460	6.00	8.50	12.50	17.50
1863S	157,500	4.25	6.50	11.00	22.50
1864	11,470	6.00	8.50	12.50	17.50
1864S	230,000	4.00	6.00	8.00	10.00
1865	10,500	7.00	10.00	13.00	20.00
1865S	175,000	4.00	7.00	10.00	17.50
1866	8,725	7.00	10.00	13.00	20.00
1866S	135,000	4.00	7.00	10.00	17.50
1867	6,625	7.00	10.00	15.00	22.50
1867S	140,000	4.00	7.00	10.00	17.50
1868	464,600	1.00	1.50	2.00	3.25
1868S	260,000	3.00	4.00	6.00	10.00
1869	256,600	1.00	1.50	2.00	3.25
1869S	450,000	2.50	4.00	6.00	9.00
1870	471,500	1.00	1.50	2.00	3.25
1870S	50,000	20.00	27.50	40.00	50.00
1871	907,710	1.00	1.50	2.25	3.50
1871CC	20,100	65.00	90.00	135.00	225.00
1871S	320,000	4.00	6.00	10.00	17.50
1872	2,396,450	1.00	1.25	2.25	3.50
1872CC	24,000	40.00	60.00	85.00	165.00
1872S	190,000	5.00	7.00	11.00	17.50
1873 No arrows	1,568,600	1.00	1.50	2.50	4.00
1873CC No arrows	12,400	Unique			
1873 With arrows	2,378,500	5.00	7.00	10.00	18.00
1873CC With arrows	18,791	160.00	275.00	375.00	500.00
1873S With arrows	455,000	7.00	10.00	15.00	22.50
1874 With arrows	2,940,700	4.50	6.50	9.50	18.50
1874CC With arrows	10,817	45.00	70.00	105.00	210.00
1874S With arrows	240,000	8.00	10.00	16.00	27.50
1875	10,350,700	.85	1.35	1.75	2.50
1875CC	4,645,000	1.00	1.50	2.25	4.50
1875S	9,070,000	1.00	1.35	2.00	3.50
1876	11,461,150	.85	1.35	1.75	2.50
1876CC	8,270,000	1.00	1.50	2.25	4.50
1876S	10,420,000	1.00	1.35	2.00	3.50
1877	7,310,510	.85	1.35	1.75	2.50
1877CC	7,700,000	1.00	1.35	2.00	3.50
1877S	2,340,000	1.00	1.35	2.00	3.50
1878	1,678,800	1.00	1.35	2.00	3.50
1878CC	200,000	6.00	8.00	12.00	17.50
1879	15,100	6.00	7.00	11.00	15.00
1880	37,355	5.00	7.00	8.00	10.00
1881	24,975	5.00	7.00	8.00	10.00
1882	3,911,100	.85	1.35	1.75	2.50
1883	7,675,712	.85	1.35	1.75	2.50
1884	3,366,380	.85	1.35	1.75	2.50
1884S	564,969	3.50	5.00	7.00	13.00
1885	2,533,427	.85	1.35	1.75	2.50
1885S	43,690	30.00	40.00	55.00	90.00
1886	6,377,570	.85	1.35	1.75	2.50
1886S	206,524	4.00	5.00	7.50	12.50
1887	11,283,939	.85	1.35	1.75	2.50

DIMES

	Quan. Minted	Good	V. Good	Fine	V. Fine
1887S	4,454,450	$1.00	$1.50	$2.25	$4.00
1888	5,496,487	.85	1.35	1.75	2.50
1888S	1,720,000	1.50	2.00	3.00	4.50
1889	7,380,711	.85	1.35	1.75	2.50
1889S	972,678	4.00	6.00	8.00	22.00
1890	9,911,541	.85	1.35	1.75	2.50
1890S	1,423,076	1.50	2.00	3.00	4.50
1891	15,310,600	.85	1.35	1.75	2.50
1891O	4,540,000	1.10	1.65	2.75	7.00
1891S	3,196,116	1.00	1.50	2.25	4.00

BARBER OR LIBERTY HEAD TYPE 1892-1916

GOOD—*Date and letters plain. LIBERTY over brow is obliterated.*
FINE—*All letters in LIBERTY visible though some are weak.*
V. FINE—*All letters of LIBERTY evenly plain.*

	Quan. Minted	Good	Fine	V. Fine
1892	12,121,245	$ .50	$ 1.25	$ 2.00
1892O	3,841,700	1.25	2.00	3.00
1892S	990,710	7.50	12.00	17.50
1893	3,340,792	.75	1.50	2.25
1893O	1,760,000	1.75	3.50	5.50
1893S	2,491,401	1.75	3.50	5.50
1894	1,330,972	1.50	2.50	4.00
1894O	720,000	11.00	30.00	40.00
1894S	24	—	—	—
1895	690,880	11.00	19.00	30.00
1895O	440,000	22.50	50.00	75.00
1895S	1,120,000	3.50	7.00	12.00
1896	2,000,762	1.25	2.50	3.50
1896O	610,000	9.00	20.00	30.00
1896S	575,056	12.00	22.00	35.00
1897	10,869,264	.40	.90	1.75
1897O	666,000	8.00	17.50	27.50
1897S	1,342,844	2.50	6.50	11.00
1898	16,320,735	.35	.75	1.10
1898O	2,130,000	1.25	3.50	9.00
1898S	1,702,507	1.25	3.50	8.00
1899	19,580,846	.25	.60	1.00
1899O	2,650,000	1.25	3.50	8.00
1899S	1,867,493	1.25	3.50	6.50
1900	17,600,912	.25	.50	1.00
1900O	2,010,000	1.00	3.00	6.00
1900S	5,168,270	.75	2.50	3.50
1901	18,860,478	.25	.50	1.00
1901O	5,620,000	.50	2.50	5.00
1901S	593,022	9.00	35.00	65.00
1902	21,380,777	.25	.50	1.00
1902O	4,500,000	.50	2.00	4.00
1902S	2,070,000	1.25	3.50	7.00
1903	19,500,755	.25	.50	1.00
1903O	8,180,000	.35	2.00	3.50
1903S	613,300	5.00	11.00	18.00
1904	14,601,027	.25	.50	1.00

DIMES

	Quan. Minted	Good	Fine	V. Fine
1904S	800,000	$4.50	$9.00	$17.50
1905	14,552,350	.25	.50	1.00
1905O	3,400,000	.50	1.75	3.50
1905S	6,855,199	.40	1.75	3.00
1906	19,958,406	.20	.40	.75
1906D	4,060,000	.50	1.00	1.75
1906O	2,610,000	.75	1.50	2.50
1906S	3,136,640	.75	1.50	2.50
1907	22,220,575	.20	.40	.75
1907D	4,080,000	.40	1.00	2.00
1907O	5,058,000	.40	1.00	2.00
1907S	3,178,470	.50	1.00	2.25
1908	10,600,545	.20	.40	.70
1908D	7,490,000	.20	.40	.70
1908O	1,789,000	1.00	2.00	3.00
1908S	3,220,000	.50	1.25	2.25
1909	10,240,650	.20	.40	.75
1909D	954,000	1.25	3.00	5.00
1909O	2,287,000	.75	2.75	4.50
1909S	1,000,000	1.00	3.00	5.00
1910	11,520,551	.20	.35	.60
1910D	3,490,000	.40	.75	1.10
1910S	1,240,000	.75	1.50	2.50
1911	18,870,543	.20	.35	.60
1911D	11,209,000	.20	.50	1.00
1911S	3,520,000	.40	.85	1.50
1912	19,350,700	.20	.35	.60
1912D	11,760,000	.20	.50	1.00
1912S	3,420,000	.40	1.50	2.50
1913	19,760,622	.20	.35	.60
1913S	510,000	3.00	10.00	16.00
1914	17,360,655	.20	.35	.60
1914D	11,908,000	.20	.40	.75
1914S	2,100,000	.50	1.50	2.50
1915	5,620,450	.20	.50	1.00
1915S	960,000	.75	1.50	2.50
1916 Old Type	18,490,000	.20	.35	.75
1916S Old type	5,820,000	.20	.50	1.00

WINGED LIBERTY HEAD or "MERCURY" TYPE 1916-1945

GOOD—Letters and dates clear. Lines and diagonal bands in fasces are obliterated.

FINE—All sticks in fasces are defined. Diagonal bands worn at center high points only.

V. FINE—Diagonal bands show where they cross fasces.

	Quan. Minted	Good	Fine	V. Fine
1916 New type (Mercury Head)	22,180,080	.15	.45	.75
1916D New type	264,000	55.00	110.00	150.00
1916S New type	10,450,000	.45	1.10	1.75
1917	55,230,000	.15	.25	.40
1917D	9,402,000	.70	2.00	4.00
1917S	27,330,000	.15	.45	1.10
1918	26,680,000	.15	.45	1.10
1918D	22,674,800	.20	1.00	2.00
1918S	19,300,000	.20	.90	1.75

DIMES

	Quan. Minted	Good	Fine	V. Fine
1919	35,740,000	$ .15	$ .45	$1.10
1919D	9,939,000	.60	2.75	5.50
1919S	8,850,000	.60	2.75	5.50
1920	59,030,000	.15	.30	.70
1920D	19,171,000	.20	.80	2.00
1920S	13,820,000	.20	.80	2.00
1921	1,230,000	6.50	20.00	39.00
1921D	1,080,000	9.50	26.50	45.00
1923	50,130,000	.15	.25	.40
1923S	6,440,000	.50	1.75	3.25
1924	24,010,000	.15	.25	.40
1924D	6,810,000	.25	.90	2.00
1924S	7,120,000	.25	.90	2.25
1925	25,610,000	.15	.25	.45
1925D	5,117,000	.80	2.25	6.50
1925S	5,850,000	.25	.90	2.00
1926	32,160,000	.15	.25	.40
1926D	6,828,000	.25	1.00	1.75
1926S	1,520,000	2.10	5.25	9.50
1927	28,080,000	.15	.25	.40
1927D	4,812,000	.35	1.75	4.00
1927S	4,770,000	.25	1.00	2.50
1928	19,480,000	.12	.20	.40
1928D	4,161,000	.25	1.00	2.00
1928S	7,400,000	.20	.60	1.50
1929	25,970,000	.12	.20	.35
1929D	5,034,000	.15	.30	.60
1929S	4,730,000	.15	.30	.60
1930	6,770,000	.15	.30	.60
1930S	1,843,000	.90	1.75	2.75
1931	3,150,000	.40	.80	1.50
1931D	1,260,000	2.00	3.75	6.50
1931S	1,800,000	1.25	2.25	3.50
1934	24,080,000	.11	.11	.20
1934D	6,772,000	.11	.20	.35
1935	58,830,000	.11	.11	.12
1935D	10,477,000	.11	.20	.35
1935S	15,840,000	.11	.12	.15

Proof quantities shown in parentheses

	Quan. Minted			V. Fine
1936 (4,130)	87,504,130			.11
1936D	16,132,000			.13
1936S	9,210,000			.15
1937 (5,756)	56,865,756			.11
1937D	14,146,000			.13
1937S	9,740,000			.15
1938 (8,728)	22,198,728			.11
1938D	5,537,000			.15
1938S	8,090,000			.15
1939 (9,321)	67,749,321			.11
1939D	24,394,000			.11
1939S	10,540,000			.15
1940 (11,827)	65,361,827			.11
1940D	21,198,000			.11
1940S	21,560,000			.11
1941 (16,557)	175,106,557			.11

DIMES

	Quan. Minted	Good	Fine	V. Fine
1941D	45,634,000			$ .11
1941S	43,090,000			.11
1942 Normal date (22,329)	205,432,329			.11
1942 2 over 1 (Error, see picture p. 14)		$45.00	$60.00	85.00
1942D	60,740,000			.11
1942S	49,300,000			.11
1943	191,710,000			.11
1943D	71,949,000			.11
1943S	60,400,000			.11
1944	231,410,000			.11
1944D	62,224,000			.11
1944S	49,490,000			.11
1945	159,130,000			.11
1945D	40,245,000			.11
1945S	41,920,000			.11

ROOSEVELT TYPE 1946 to Date

FINE—Torch flame smooth. Vertical lines in torch show, horizontal lines smooth.

V. FINE—All vertical lines on torch will show.

	Quan. Minted	Fine	V. Fine
1946	255,250,000	.11	.11
1946D	61,043,500	.11	.11
1946S	27,900,000	.12	.15
1947	121,520,000	.11	.11
1947D	46,835,000	.11	.11
1947S	34,840,000	.11	.11
1948	74,950,000	.11	.11
1948D	52,841,000	.11	.11
1948S	35,520,000	.11	.11
1949	30,940,000	.11	.20
1949D	26,034,000	.11	.11
1949S	13,510,000	.25	.40
1950 (51,386)	50,181,500	.11	.11
1950D	46,803,000	.11	.11
1950S	20,440,000	.12	.15
1951 (57,500)	103,937,602	.11	.11
1951D	56,529,000	.11	.11
1951S	31,630,000	.12	.15
1952 (81,980)	99,122,073	.11	.11
1952D	122,100,000	.11	.11
1952S	44,419,500	.11	.11
1953 (128,800)	53,618,920	.11	.11
1953D	136,433,000	.11	.11
1953S	39,180,000	.11	.11
1954 (233,300)	114,243,503	.11	.11
1954D	106,397,000	.11	.11
1954S	22,860,000	.11	.11
1955 (378,200)	12,828,381	.15	.25
1955D	13,959,000	.15	.20
1955S	18,510,000	.12	.15

Dimes prior to 1956 command a premium if in bright uncirculated condition.

ROOSEVELT DIMES

Quan. Minted	V. Fine
1956 (669,384)...109,309,384	$ .11
1956D...........108,015,100	.11
1957 (1,247,952)..161,407,952	.11
1957D...........113,354,330	.11
1958 (875,652).....32,785,652	.11
1958D...........136,564,600	.11
1959 (1,149,291)...86,929,291	.11
1959D...........164,919,790	.11
1960 (1,691,602)...72,081,602	.11
1960D...........200,160,400	.11
1961 (3,028,244)...96,758,244	.11
1961D...........209,146,550	.11
1962 (3,218,019)...75,668,019	.11
1962D...........334,948,380	.11
1963 (3,075,645)..126,725,645	.11
1963D...........421,476,530	.11
1964 (3,950,762)..933,310,762	.11
1964D.........1,357,517,180	.11

CLAD COINAGE

Quan. Minted	V. Fine
1965...........1,652,140,570	$ .10
1966...........1,382,734,540	.10
1967...... 2,244,007,320	.10
1968...........424,470,400	.10
1968D...........480,748,280	.10
1968S Proof only...3,041,509	.60
1969...........145,790,000	.10
1969D...........563,323,870	.10
1969S Proof only...2,934,631	.60
1970...........345,570,000	.10
1970D...........754,942,100	.10
1970S Proof only...2,632,810	.60
1971......................	.10
1971D....................	.10
1971S Proof only...........	.60

TWENTY-CENT PIECES
(Coined from 1875 to 1878)

This series was a short-lived coinage experiment; soon after their appearance the populace complained about the similarity in design and size to the quarter-dollar. The 1876CC mint piece is a great rarity, only about ten being in existence. 1877 and 1878 were struck in proof only.

GOOD—*LIBERTY on shield obliterated. Letters and date legible.*

V. GOOD—*At least 3 letters of LIBERTY show.*

FINE—*LIBERTY completely readable, but partly weak.*

V. FINE—*All letters of LIBERTY bold.*

	Quan. Minted	Good	V. Good	Fine	V. Fine
1875.........................39,700		$13.00	$17.00	$22.50	$30.00
1875CC......................133,290		14.00	18.00	24.00	35.00
1875S......................1,155,000		12.00	15.00	20.00	25.00
1876.........................15,900		15.00	19.00	25.00	35.00
1876CC (Only about 10 known)..10,000					
1877 Proofs only.................510				Proof	425.00
1878 Proofs only.................600				Proof	325.00

QUARTER DOLLARS
Issued from 1796 to date

The first date, 1796, follows the pattern of the early half dimes and dimes by the absence of a mark of value. In 1804 a "25 C" was added to the reverse. This mark of value was used until 1838 when "Quar. Dol." appeared although there was sufficient room for a complete spelling of the denomination. It was not until the adoption of the Barber (erroneously called "Morgan") type in 1892 that the value is spelled out entirely.

QUARTER DOLLARS

DRAPED BUST TYPE, SMALL EAGLE REVERSE 1796

	Quan. Minted	Fair	Good	V. Good	Fine	V. Fine
1796	6,146	$275.00	$450.00	$750.00	$1275.00	$1675.00

DRAPED BUST TYPE, HERALDIC EAGLE REVERSE 1804-1807

1804	6,738	50.00	85.00	110.00	225.00	375.00
1805	121,394	25.00	40.00	47.50	80.00	150.00
1806	206,124	20.00	30.00	45.00	60.00	125.00
1807	220,643	20.00	30.00	45.00	60.00	125.00

CAPPED BUST TYPE 1815-1838

Variety 1 — Large size, motto above eagle 1815-1828

1815	89,235	8.50	12.00	17.50	30.00	80.00
1818	361,174	8.00	11.00	14.00	24.00	40.00
1819	144,000	8.00	11.00	14.00	24.00	37.50
1820	127,444	8.00	11.00	14.00	24.00	37.50
1821	216,851	8.00	11.00	14.00	24.00	37.50
1822 Rev. 25 over 50	} 64,080	70.00	80.00	110.00	185.00	260.00
Normal rev.		8.00	11.00	14.00	24.00	37.50
1823 All 3 over 2	17,800	250.00	400.00	525.00	750.00	1400.00

QUARTER DOLLARS

	Quan. Minted	Fair	Good	V. Good	Fine	V. Fine
1824	———	$10.00	$15.00	$22.50	$35.00	$55.00
1825	168,000	8.00	11.00	14.00	24.00	37.50
1827 Originals (Rare)	4,000					———
Restrikes (Rare)						———
1828	102,000	8.00	11.00	14.00	24.00	37.50

Variety 2 — Reduced size, no motto 1831-1838

GOOD—*Bust is well defined. Hair under headband is smooth. Date, letters, stars readable. Scant rims.*

V. GOOD—*Details apparent but worn on high spots. Rim strong. Full LIBERTY.*

FINE—*All hairlines visible. Drapery partly worn. Shoulder clasp distinct.*

V. FINE—*Only top spots worn. Clasp sharp. Ear distinct.*

	Quan. Minted	Good	V. Good	Fine	V. Fine
1831	398,000	7.00	9.00	13.00	25.00
1832	320,000	7.00	9.00	13.00	25.00
1833	156,000	8.00	10.00	15.00	26.00
1834	286,000	7.00	9.00	13.00	25.00
1835	1,952,000	7.00	9.00	13.00	25.00
1836	472,000	7.00	9.00	13.00	25.00
1837	252,400	7.00	9.00	13.00	25.00
1838	Both types 832,000	7.00	9.00	13.00	25.00

LIBERTY SEATED TYPE 1838-1891
Variety 1 — No motto above eagle 1838-1853

GOOD—*Scant rim. LIBERTY on shield worn off. Date and letters readable.*

V. GOOD—*Rim fairly defined, at least 3 letters in LIBERTY evident.*

FINE—*Liberty complete, but partly weak.*

V. FINE—*LIBERTY strong.*

		Good	V. Good	Fine	V. Fine
1838 Liberty Seated		3.50	5.00	7.50	13.00
1839	491,146	2.50	4.00	6.50	12.00
1840O All kinds	425,200	2.50	4.00	6.50	12.00
1840 Drapery to elbow	188,127	2.50	4.00	6.50	12.00
1840O Drapery to elbow		2.50	4.00	6.50	12.00
1841	120,000	6.25	8.25	12.00	20.00
1841O	452,000	2.50	3.50	4.50	9.00
1842	88,000	2.50	3.50	4.50	9.00
1842O	769,000	2.50	3.50	4.50	9.00
1843	645,600	2.00	3.00	4.00	7.00
1843O	968,000	2.00	3.00	4.00	7.00
1844	421,200	2.00	3.00	4.00	7.00
1844O	740,000	2.00	3.00	4.00	7.00
1845	922,000	2.00	3.00	4.00	7.00
1846	510,000	2.00	3.00	4.00	7.00
1847	734,000	2.00	3.00	4.00	7.00
1847O	368,000	2.00	3.00	4.00	7.00

[55]

QUARTER DOLLARS

	Quan. Minted	Good	V. Good	Fine	V. Fine
1848	146,000	$ 2.25	$ 3.25	$ 4.50	$ 7.50
1849	340,000	2.00	3.00	4.00	7.00
1849O	——	32.50	47.50	70.00	100.00
1850	190,800	2.25	3.25	4.50	7.50
1850O	412,000	2.00	3.00	4.00	7.00
1851	160,000	2.00	3.00	4.00	7.00
1851O	88,000	2.25	3.50	5.00	11.00
1852	177,060	2.00	3.00	4.00	7.00
1852O	96,000	3.75	5.50	8.00	15.00
1853 Recut date, no arrows and rays (Beware altered 1858)	44,200	25.00	30.00	52.50	80.00

Variety 2 — Arrows at date, rays around eagle 1853 only

1853 Arrows and rays	15,210,020	2.75	3.75	5.00	10.00
1853O Arrows and rays	1,332,000	4.00	6.00	8.25	15.00

Variety 3 — Arrows at date, no rays 1854-1855

1854	12,380,000	2.00	2.50	4.00	7.00
1854O	1,484,000	2.25	2.75	4.50	7.50
1855	2,857,000	2.00	2.50	4.00	7.00
1855O	176,000	22.00	27.50	42.50	75.00
1855S	396,400	22.00	27.50	42.50	75.00

Variety 1 resumed 1856-1865

1856	7,264,000	1.75	2.50	3.25	4.25
1856O	968,000	2.00	2.50	3.75	5.00
1856S	286,000	9.00	14.00	21.00	45.00
1857	9,644,000	1.75	2.50	3.25	4.25
1857O	1,180,000	2.00	2.50	3.75	5.00
1857S	82,000	10.00	15.00	21.00	45.00
1858	7,368,000	1.75	2.50	3.25	4.25
1858O	520,000	2.25	2.75	4.25	6.00
1858S	121,000	12.50	15.00	21.00	40.00
1859	1,344,000	1.75	2.50	3.25	4.25
1859O	260,000	2.25	2.75	4.25	6.00
1859S	80,000	12.50	15.00	21.00	40.00
1860	805,400	1.75	2.50	3.25	4.25
1860O	388,000	2.00	2.50	3.75	5.00
1860S	56,000	8.50	10.00	15.00	35.00
1861	4,854,600	1.75	2.50	3.25	4.25

QUARTER DOLLARS

	Quan. Minted	Good	V. Good	Fine	V. Fine
1861S	96,000	$8.00	$11.00	$16.00	$32.50
1862	932,550	1.75	2.50	3.25	4.25
1862S	67,000	6.50	8.50	10.00	25.00
1863	192,060	1.75	2.50	3.25	4.25
1864	94,070	1.75	2.50	3.25	4.25
1864S	20,000	10.00	20.00	30.00	50.00
1865	59,300	2.00	2.50	3.75	5.00
1865S	41,000	5.50	7.50	11.00	22.50

Variety 4 —
Motto above eagle
1866-1873

		Good	V. Good	Fine	V. Fine
1866 With motto —					
(In God We Trust)	17,525	2.65	3.25	4.65	7.00
1866S With motto	28,000	7.25	8.25	11.50	27.50
1867	20,625	2.25	3.00	4.25	6.00
1867S	48,000	6.00	8.00	11.00	22.00
1868	30,000	2.50	3.25	4.25	6.00
1868S	96,000	5.50	7.00	8.50	20.00
1869	16,600	2.75	3.25	5.50	9.00
1869S	76,000	6.00	7.50	8.50	20.00
1870	87,400	1.75	2.50	3.25	4.50
1870CC	8,340	70.00	85.00	110.00	210.00
1871	119,160	1.75	2.50	3.00	3.75
1871CC	10,890	65.00	75.00	95.00	150.00
1871S	30,900	4.50	6.50	11.00	20.00
1872	182,950	1.75	2.50	3.00	3.75
1872CC	9,100	75.00	95.00	135.00	250.00
1872S	83,000	7.00	10.00	15.00	25.00
1873 Without arrows	212,600	3.50	5.00	7.50	10.00
1873CC Without arrows	4,000	275.00	350.00	450.00	650.00
Variety 5 — Arrows at date 1873-1874					
1873 Arrows	1,271,700	10.00	12.50	16.00	27.50
1873CC Arrows	12,462	180.00	225.00	325.00	550.00
1873S Arrows	156,000	12.50	16.00	21.00	32.50
1874 Arrows	471,900	10.00	12.50	16.00	27.50
1874S Arrows	392,000	12.50	16.00	21.00	32.50
Variety 4 resumed 1875-1891					
1875	4,293,500	1.75	2.50	3.00	3.75
1875CC	140,000	4.00	5.50	8.00	14.00
1875S	680,000	4.00	5.50	8.00	14.00
1876	17,817,150	1.75	2.50	3.00	3.75
1876CC	4,944,000	2.00	2.50	3.25	5.50
1876S	8,596,000	1.75	2.50	3.00	3.75
1877	10,911,710	1.75	2.50	3.00	3.75
1877CC	4,192,000	2.00	2.50	3.25	5.50

QUARTER DOLLARS

	Quan. Minted	Good	V. Good	Fine	V. Fine
1877S	8,996,000	$ 1.75	$ 2.50	$ 3.00	$ 3.75
1878	2,260,800	1.75	2.50	3.00	3.75
1878CC	996,000	3.25	4.00	5.00	8.50
1878S	140,000	65.00	90.00	125.00	200.00
1879	14,700	7.50	9.00	11.00	14.00
1880	14,955	7.50	9.00	11.00	13.00
1881	12,975	7.50	9.00	11.00	13.00
1882	16,300	7.00	8.25	10.00	12.00
1883	15,439	7.00	8.25	10.00	12.00
1884	8,875	10.00	12.00	14.00	16.00
1885	14,530	7.50	9.00	11.00	13.00
1886	5,886	13.00	15.00	18.00	23.00
1887	10,710	7.50	9.00	11.00	14.00
1888	10,833	7.50	9.00	11.00	14.00
1888S	1,216,000	1.75	2.25	3.00	4.50
1889	12,711	7.50	9.00	11.00	13.00
1890	80,590	2.00	2.75	3.50	4.75
1891	3,920,600	1.75	2.50	3.00	3.75
1891O	68,000	40.00	50.00	60.00	100.00
(Only date of this type struck at New Orleans Mint.)					
1891S	2,216,000	2.00	2.50	3.25	5.50

BARBER or LIBERTY HEAD TYPE 1892-1916

GOOD—Date and legends readable. LIBER-TY worn off of headband.

V. GOOD—Minimum of 3 letters in LIBERTY readable.

FINE—LIBERTY completely readable but not sharp.

V. FINE—All letters in LIBERTY evenly plain.

1892	8,237,245	.50	.60	1.00	3.00
1892O	2,640,000	1.50	1.85	2.50	5.00
1892S	964,079	5.00	7.00	11.00	18.00
1893	5,444,815	.50	.65	1.00	2.50
1893O	3,396,000	.90	1.45	2.00	4.00
1893S	1,454,535	1.50	2.25	3.25	5.50
1894	3,432,972	.60	1.00	1.25	3.00
1894O	2,852,000	1.00	1.65	2.50	4.50
1894S	2,648,821	1.00	1.50	2.50	5.00
1895	4,440,880	.50	.70	1.00	2.00
1895O	2,816,000	1.00	1.65	2.50	6.00
1895S	1,764,681	1.50	2.25	3.25	5.50
1896	3,874,762	.50	.80	1.15	2.50
1896O	1,484,000	2.00	3.75	6.00	12.00
1896S	188,039	40.00	70.00	105.00	160.00
1897	8,140,731	.40	.65	1.00	2.25
1897O	1,414,800	3.00	4.50	7.00	12.00
1897S	542,229	3.50	5.25	8.00	12.00
1898	11,100,735	.40	.65	1.00	2.00
1898O	1,868,000	1.00	1.50	2.50	5.50
1898S	1,020,592	1.00	1.85	3.00	5.50

QUARTER DOLLARS

	Quan. Minted	Good	V. Good	Fine	V. Fine
1899	12,624,846	$ .40	$ .60	$ .85	$2.25
1899O	2,644,000	.85	1.65	2.50	4.75
1899S	708,000	3.00	4.00	5.50	7.50
1900	10,016,912	.40	.60	1.00	2.25
1900O	3,416,000	1.25	1.85	3.00	6.00
1900S	1,858,585	.75	1.60	3.00	6.50
1901	8,892,813	.40	.55	.75	1.75
1901O	1,612,000	4.00	7.00	12.50	20.00
1901S	72,664	110.00	160.00	240.00	350.00
1902	12,197,744	.40	.55	.75	1.75
1902O	4,748,000	.80	1.65	3.25	6.50
1902S	1,524,612	1.60	2.75	4.50	7.50
1903	9,670,064	.40	.55	.75	1.75
1903O	3,500,000	.90	2.10	4.00	8.00
1903S	1,036,000	2.00	2.75	4.50	10.00
1904	9,588,813	.40	.55	.75	1.75
1904O	2,456,000	2.25	4.00	6.50	12.00
1905	4,968,250	.50	.75	1.00	2.50
1905O	1,230,000	2.25	3.75	6.00	10.00
1905S	1,884,000	1.50	2.50	3.50	6.00
1906	3,656,435	.50	.75	1.00	2.50
1906D	3,280,000	.60	.95	1.50	2.50
1906O	2,056,000	.75	1.10	1.75	2.50
1907	7,192,575	.40	.55	.75	1.75
1907D	2,484,000	.65	.95	1.50	2.25
1907O	4,560,000	.60	.85	1.25	2.00
1907S	1,360,000	.80	1.50	2.25	4.50
1908	4,232,545	.40	.65	1.00	2.00
1908D	5,788,000	.40	.65	1.00	2.00
1908O	6,244,000	.40	.55	.75	2.25
1908S	784,000	2.00	3.50	5.00	7.50
1909	9,268,650	.40	.55	.75	1.75
1909D	5,114,000	.40	.65	1.00	2.00
1909O	712,000	4.50	8.00	13.50	20.00
1909S	1,348,000	.75	1.50	2.25	4.25
1910	2,244,551	.45	.70	1.00	1.75
1910D	1,500,000	.75	1.20	1.75	2.75
1911	3,720,543	.40	.55	.75	1.75
1911D	933,600	.75	1.50	2.25	4.50
1911S	988,000	.90	1.60	2.50	5.00
1912	4,400,700	.40	.55	.75	1.75
1912S	708,000	1.25	2.25	3.50	7.50
1913	484,613	2.00	3.00	4.00	7.00
1913D	1,450,800	.80	1.40	2.00	3.25
1913S	40,000	40.00	65.00	110.00	140.00
1914	6,244,610	.40	.55	.75	1.75
1914D	3,046,000	.40	.55	.75	1.75
1914S	264,000	3.00	5.25	7.50	17.50
1915	3,480,450	.40	.55	.75	1.75
1915D	3,694,000	.40	.55	.75	1.75
1915S	704,000	.60	1.00	1.50	3.00
1916	1,788,000	.40	.75	1.25	2.25
1916D	6,540,800	.40	.55	.75	1.75

QUARTER DOLLARS
STANDING LIBERTY TYPE 1916-1930
Variety 1 — No stars below eagle 1916-1917

GOOD—*Date and lettering readable. Top of date worn. Liberty's right leg and toes worn off.*

V. GOOD—*Distinct date. Toes show faintly. Drapery lines visible above her left leg.*

FINE—*High curve of right leg flat from thigh to ankle.*

V. FINE—*Garment line worn but shows at sides. (Some modifications must be made for grading variety 2.)*

	Quan. Minted	Good	V. Good	Fine	V. Fine
1916	52,000	$140.00	$180.00	$250.00	$325.00
1917	8,792,000	1.75	2.00	3.00	4.50
1917D	1,509,200	2.50	3.50	5.00	7.00
1917S	1,952,000	2.50	3.50	5.00	7.00

Variety 2 — Stars below eagle 1917-1930

	Quan. Minted	Good	V. Good	Fine	V. Fine
1917	13,880,000	1.50	2.15	3.25	5.50
1917D	6,224,400	3.25	4.75	7.00	11.00
1917S	5,552,000	3.75	5.00	7.50	12.00
1918	14,240,000	1.75	2.50	3.50	6.00
1918D	7,380,000	3.00	4.25	5.50	8.00
1918S Normal date	11,072,000	1.75	2.50	4.00	6.50
1918S 8 over 7 (See page 13)		125.00	175.00	225.00	325.00
1919	11,324,000	2.00	2.90	4.00	6.00
1919D	1,944,000	11.00	15.00	20.00	32.50
1919S	1,836,000	12.00	17.00	22.50	35.00
1920	27,860,000	1.75	2.00	2.75	4.00
1920D	3,586,400	4.00	6.00	9.00	15.00
1920S	6,380,000	3.00	4.00	5.00	10.00
1921	1,916,000	9.50	14.00	19.00	27.50
1923	9,716,000	1.00	1.50	2.25	3.75
1923S*	1,360,000	17.50	22.50	27.50	40.00
1924	10,920,000	1.00	1.50	2.25	4.00
1924D	3,112,000	3.00	4.25	5.50	9.00
1924S	2,860,000	4.00	5.75	8.00	12.00
1925	12,280,000	.40	.65	1.00	2.00
1926	11,316,000	.40	.55	.90	1.75
1926D	1,716,000	.50	.70	1.00	2.00
1926S	2,700,000	.90	1.40	2.25	6.00
1927	11,912,000	.40	.50	.75	1.75
1927D	976,400	1.00	1.40	1.75	3.00
1927S	396,000	2.50	3.25	6.50	12.50

*Beware altered date.

QUARTER DOLLARS

	Quan. Minted	Good	V. Good	Fine	V. Fine
1928	6,336,000	$ .40	$ .50	$ .75	$1.50
1928D	1,627,600	.40	.50	.75	1.50
1928S	2,644,000	.40	.50	.75	1.50
1929	11,140,000	.40	.50	.75	1.50
1929D	1,358,000	.40	.50	.75	1.50
1929S	1,764,000	.40	.50	.75	1.50
1930	5,632,000	.40	.50	.75	1.50
1930S	1,556,000	.40	.50	.75	1.50

Liberty standing quarters minted from 1916 to 1924 are scarce in any condition. The quarters struck during this period had the date in the same position as later issues, but because that part of the coin was high it received much wear and after a few years in circulation became obliterated. Since 1924 the date has been "recessed," thereby permitting coin to wear and date remain legible.

WASHINGTON TYPE 1932 to Date

Variety 1 — Silver 1932-1964

Quarters dated prior to 1956 command a premium if in bright uncirculated condition.

GOOD—Letters and date flat, but separated from rim. No hairlines near face.

V. GOOD—Wing-tips outlined. Rims on both sides are fine and even. Tops of letters at rim are flattened.

FINE—Hairlines about ear are visible. Tiny feathers on eagle's breast are faintly visible.

V. FINE—Hair details worn but plain. Feathers at sides of eagle's breast are plain.

1932	5,404,000	.30	.45	.60	.85
1932D	436,800	17.50	25.00	27.50	30.00
1932S	408,000	17.50	23.00	25.00	27.50
1934	31,912,052	.28	.28	.30	.35
1934D	3,527,200	.35	.50	1.00	2.00
1935	32,484,000	.28	.28	.30	.35
1935D	5,780,000	.28	.35	.75	1.50
1935S	5,660,000	.28	.35	.50	.85
1936 (3,837)	41,303,837	.28	.28	.30	.35
1936D	5,374,000	.35	.50	1.75	4.00
1936S	3,828,000	.28	.30	.45	.75
1937 (5,542)	19,701,542	.28	.28	.28	.30
1937D	7,189,600	.28	.30	.45	.75
1937S	1,652,000	1.25	3.00	4.00	5.00
1938 (8,045)	9,480,045	.28	.35	.70	1.25
1938S	2,832,000	.40	.70	1.10	1.75
1939 (8,795)	33,548,795	.28	.28	.28	.30
1939D	7,092,000	.28	.30	.45	.75
1939S	2,628,000	.40	.75	1.20	2.00
1940 (11,246)	35,715,246	.28	.28	.28	.30
1940D	2,797,600	.30	.50	1.00	1.75
1940S	8,244,000	.28	.28	.30	.35
1941 (15,287)	79,047,287	.28	.28	.28	.30

QUARTER DOLLARS

	Quan. Minted	Good	V. Good	Fine	V. Fine
1941D...................	16,714,800	$ .28	$ .28	$ .28	$ .30
1941S...................	16,080,000	.28	.28	.28	.30
1942 (21,123)............	102,117,123	.28	.28	.28	.28
1942D...................	17,487,200	.28	.28	.28	.28
1942S...................	19,384,000	.28	.28	.28	.28
1943....................	99,700,000	.28	.28	.28	.28
1943D...................	16,095,600	.28	.28	.28	.28
1943S...................	21,700,000	.28	.28	.28	.28
1944....................	104,956,000	.28	.28	.28	.28
1944D...................	14,600,800	.28	.28	.28	.28
1944S...................	12,560,000	.28	.28	.28	.28
1945....................	74,372,000	.28	.28	.28	.28
1945D...................	12,341,600	.28	.28	.28	.28
1945S...................	17,004,001	.28	.28	.28	.28
1946....................	53,436,000	.28	.28	.28	.28
1946D...................	9,072,800	.28	.28	.28	.28
1946S...................	4,204,000	.30	.35	.40	.50
1947....................	22,556,000	.28	.28	.28	.28
1947D...................	15,338,400	.28	.28	.28	.28
1947S...................	5,532,000	.30	.35	.40	.45
1948....................	35,196,000		.28	.28	.28
1948D...................	16,766,800		.28	.28	.28
1948S...................	15,960,000		.28	.28	.28
1949....................	9,312,000		.28	.30	.50
1949D...................	10,068,400		.28	.28	.28
1950 (51,386)............	24,971,512		.28	.28	.28
1950D...................	21,075,600		.28	.28	.28
1950S...................	10,284,004		.28	.28	.28
1951 (57,500)............	43,505,602		.28	.28	.28
1951D...................	35,354,800		.28	.28	.28
1951S...................	8,948,000		.28	.28	.28
1952 (81,980)............	38,862,073		.28	.28	.28
1952D...................	49,795,200		.28	.28	.28
1952S...................	13,707,800		.28	.28	.28
1953 (128,800)...........	18,664,920		.28	.28	.28
1953D...................	56,112,400		.28	.28	.28
1953S...................	14,016,000		.28	.28	.28
1954 (233,300)...........	54,645,503		.28	.28	.28
1954D...................	46,305,500		.28	.28	.28
1954S...................	11,834,722		.28	.28	.28
1955 (378,200)...........	18,558,381		.28	.28	.28
1955D...................	3,182,400		.50	.85	1.25
1956 (669,384)...........	44,813,384			.28	.28
1956D...................	32,334,500			.28	.28
1957 (1,247,952)..........	47,779,952			.28	.28
1957D...................	77,924,160			.28	.28
1958 (875,652)...........	7,235,652			.28	.40
1958D...................	78,124,900			.28	.28
1959 (1,149,291)..........	25,533,291			.28	.28
1959D...................	62,054,232			.28	.28
1960 (1,691,602)	30,855,602			.28	.28
1960D...................	63,000,324			.28	.28
1961 (3,028,244)	37,036,000			.28	.28
1961D...................	83,656,928			.28	.28

QUARTER DOLLARS

	Quan. Minted	V.F.		Quan. Minted	V.F.
1962 (3,218,019)...	39,374,019	$ .28	1963D...........	135,288,184	$ .28
1962D..........	127,554,756	.28	1964 (3,950,762)..	564,341,347	.28
1963 (3,075,645)...	77,391,645	.28	1964D..........	704,135,528	.28

Variety 2 — Clad copper-nickel 1965 to date

CLAD COINAGE

1965..........	1,819,717,540	.25	1969S Proof only....	2,934,631	1.00
1966..........	821,101,500	.25	1970...........	136,420,000	.25
1967..........	1,524,031,848	.25	1970D..........	417,341,364	.25
1968..........	220,731,500	.25	1970S Proof only...	2,632,810	1.00
1968D..........	101,534,000	.25	1971............		.25
1968S Proof only...	3,041,509	1.00	1971D...........		.25
1969..........	176,212,000	.25	1971S Proof only..........		1.00
1969D..........	114,372,000	.25			

HALF DOLLARS

(Coined from 1794 to date)

A series that has been extensively collected by "varieties" and many dates contain both rare and common varieties. The collector who cares to go into the study of half dollar varieties should obtain a copy of Beistle's work on half dollars or a more recent book, *Early Half Dollar Varieties 1794-1836* by Al C. Overton.

Half dollars between about 1812 and 1840 are more or less common in ordinary circulated condition. This might be explained by the fact that the U. S. government did not issue silver dollars during this period which made the half the "big" silver money and coinage was plentiful according to standards of the time.

FLOWING HAIR TYPE 1794-1795

FAIR—Clear enough to identify.

GOOD—Date and letters sufficient to be readable. Main devices outlined, but lack details.

V. GOOD—Major details discernible. Letters well formed but worn.

FINE—Hair ends distinguishable. Top hairlines show, but otherwise worn smooth.

V. FINE—Hair in center shows some detail. Other details more bold.

	Quan. Minted	Fair	Good	V. Good	Fine	V. Fine
1794................	5,300	$80.00	$130.00	$175.00	$275.00	$500.00
1795 All kinds........	317,844					
Re-engraved date, 3 leaves under wings...		80.00	150.00	225.00	350.00	500.00
Perfect date, 2 leaves under wings...		65.00	85.00	125.00	200.00	300.00

HALF DOLLARS

DRAPED BUST TYPE, SMALL EAGLE REVERSE 1796-1797

Grading same as above for Fair to Fine.

V. FINE—*Right side of drapery slightly worn. Left side to curls is smooth.*

	Quan. Minted	Fair	Good	V. Good	Fine	V. Fine
1796 15 stars............	}	$450.00	$775.00	$1125.00	$1650.00	$2300.00
16 stars............	3,918	475.00	800.00	1175.00	1700.00	2350.00
1797.................		475.00	800.00	1175.00	1700.00	2350.00

DRAPED BUST TYPE, HERALDIC EAGLE REVERSE 1801-1807

GOOD—*Letters and date readable. E PLURIBUS UNUM obliterated.*

V. GOOD—*Motto partially readable. Only deepest drapery details visible. All other lines smooth.*

FINE—*All drapery lines distinguishable. Hairlines near cheek and neck show some detail.*

V. FINE—*Left side of drapery worn smooth.*

	Quan. Minted	Good	V. Good	Fine	V. Fine
1801........................30,289		40.00	60.00	110.00	180.00
1802........................29,890		35.00	57.50	85.00	150.00
1803.......................188,234		20.00	30.00	40.00	75.00
1805 5 over 4...............	} 211,722	30.00	40.00	60.00	100.00
Normal date...........		15.00	20.00	30.00	50.00
1806 6 over 5...............	} 839,576	20.00	25.00	35.00	70.00
6 over inverted 6........		30.00	45.00	75.00	135.00
Normal date...........		14.00	20.00	30.00	45.00
1807.......................301,076		14.00	20.00	30.00	45.00

CAPPED BUST TYPE 1807-1839

HALF DOLLARS

GOOD—Date and letters readable. Bust worn smooth with outline distinct.

V. GOOD—LIBERTY visible but faint. Legends distinguishable. Clasp at shoulder visible. Curl above it nearly smooth.

FINE—Clasp and adjacent curl clearly outlined with slight details.

V. FINE—Clasp at shoulder clear. Curl has wear only on highest point. Hair over brow distinguishable.

Variety 1 — Lettered edge 1807-1836

	Quan. Minted	Good	V. Good	Fine	V. Fine
1807 Face to left	750,500	$7.00	$10.00	$15.00	$25.00
1808 8 over 7	1,368,600	5.00	9.00	12.50	17.50
1808 Normal date		4.00	6.00	7.00	12.00
1809	1,405,810	4.00	6.00	7.00	11.50
1810	1,276,276	4.00	6.00	7.00	10.00
1811	1,203,644	3.50	6.00	7.00	10.00
1812 2 over 1	1,628,059	6.00	9.00	13.00	25.00
1812 Normal date		3.50	6.00	7.00	10.00
1813	1,241,903	3.50	6.00	7.00	10.00
1814 4 over 3	1,039,075	7.00	9.00	13.00	20.00
1814 Normal date		3.50	6.00	7.00	11.00
1815 5 over 2	47,150	40.00	60.00	90.00	120.00
1817 7 over 3		7.00	10.00	13.00	20.00
1817 dated 181.7	1,215,567	5.00	9.00	15.00	22.50
1817 Normal date		3.00	5.00	6.50	10.00
1818 8 over 7	1,960,322	3.00	5.00	6.50	10.00
1818 Normal date		3.00	5.00	6.50	9.00
1819 9 over 8	2,208,000	3.25	5.50	7.00	9.50
1819 Normal date		3.00	5.00	6.50	9.00
1820 over 19	751,122	5.00	7.00	10.00	17.50
1820 Normal date		5.00	7.00	9.00	12.50
1821	1,305,797	3.00	5.00	6.50	7.75
1822 2 over 1	1,559,573	17.00	25.00	40.00	50.00
1822 Normal date		3.00	5.00	6.50	7.75
1823	1,694,200	3.00	5.00	6.50	7.75
1824 4 over 1		3.50	6.00	7.50	10.00
1824 over other dates	3,504,954	3.00	5.00	6.50	9.00
1824 Normal date		3.00	5.00	6.50	7.75
1825	2,943,166	3.00	5.00	6.50	7.75
1826	4,004,180	3.00	5.00	6.50	7.75
1827 7 over 6	5,493,400	6.00	8.00	12.00	20.00
1827 Normal date		3.00	5.00	6.50	7.75
1828	3,075,200	3.00	5.00	6.50	7.75
1828 Curled-base, knobbed 2		17.50	22.50	30.00	45.00
1829 9 over 7	3,712,156	4.00	5.50	7.00	9.00
1829 Normal date		3.00	5.00	6.50	7.75
1830	4,764,800	3.00	5.00	6.50	7.75
1831	5,873,660	3.00	5.00	6.50	7.75
1832	4,797,000	3.00	5.00	6.50	7.75
1833	5,206,000	3.00	5.00	6.50	7.75
1834	6,412,004	3.00	5.00	6.50	7.75
1835	5,352,006	3.00	5.00	6.50	7.75
1836 Lettered edge. All kinds	6,546,200	3.00	5.00	6.50	7.75

HALF DOLLARS

Variety 2 — Reeded edge, reverse "50 CENTS" 1836-1837

GOOD—*LIBERTY discernible on head-band.*
V. GOOD—*Minimum of 3 letters in LIBERTY must be clear.*
FINE—*LIBERTY complete.*
V. FINE—*LIBERTY is sharp. Shoulder clasp is clear.*

	Quan. Minted	Good	V. Good	Fine	V. Fine
1836 Reeded edge	1,200	$20.00	$30.00	$40.00	$70.00
1837	3,629,820	7.00	10.00	17.00	25.00

Variety 3 — Reeded edge, reverse "HALF DOL." 1838-1839

The 1838O half dollar was not mentioned in Director's report. (Rufus Tyler, coiner of New Orleans Mint, stated that only 20 were coined.)

First branch mint half dollar. This and following year mint mark appears on Obv. All other years prior to 1968 (except 1916-17) mint mark is on Reverse.

1838	3,546,000	5.00	8.00	12.00	20.00
1838O	(20)				—
1839 Bust type. All kinds	3,334,560	5.00	8.00	12.00	20.00
1839O	178,976	27.50	37.50	50.00	75.00

LIBERTY SEATED TYPE 1839-1891
Variety 1 — No motto above eagle 1839-1853

GOOD—*Scant rim. LIBERTY on shield worn off. Date and letters readable.*
V. GOOD—*Rim fairly defined. At least 3 letters in LIBERTY are evident.*
FINE—*LIBERTY complete, but weak.*
V. FINE—*LIBERTY mostly sharp.*

1839 Liberty seated		4.00	5.00	7.00	12.50
1840	1,435,008	2.25	3.00	5.00	7.50
1840O	855,100	2.25	3.00	5.00	7.50
1841	310,000	3.00	4.00	6.00	11.00
1841O	401,000	2.50	3.50	5.50	8.50

HALF DOLLARS

	Quan. Minted	Good	V. Good	Fine	V. Fine
1842........................	2,012,764	$ 2.00	$ 2.75	$ 3.50	$ 6.50
1842O Small date............	} 957,000	25.00	35.00	50.00	75.00
1842O Large date............		2.00	2.75	3.50	6.50
1843........................	3,844,000	2.00	2.75	3.50	7.50
1843O......................	2,268,000	2.00	2.75	3.50	7.50
1844........................	1,766,000	2.00	2.75	3.50	7.50
1844O......................	2,005,000	2.00	2.75	3.50	7.50
1845........................	589,000	2.00	2.75	3.50	7.50
1845O......................	} 2,094,000	2.00	2.75	3.50	7.50
1845O No drapery..........		8.00	12.00	20.00	32.50
1846 Over horizontal 6 (error).	} 2,210,000	20.00	30.00	40.00	60.00
Normal date..........		2.00	2.75	3.50	7.50
1846O......................	2,304,000	2.00	2.75	3.50	7.50
1847 7 over 6..............	} 1,156,000	65.00	85.00	125.00	250.00
1847 Normal date..........		2.00	2.75	3.50	7.50
1847O......................	2,584,000	2.00	2.75	3.50	7.50
1848........................	580,000	2.00	2.75	3.50	7.50
1848O......................	3,180,000	2.00	2.75	3.50	7.50
1849........................	1,252,000	2.00	2.75	3.50	7.50
1849O......................	2,310,000	2.00	2.75	3.50	7.50
1850........................	227,000	13.50	17.00	24.00	40.00
1850O......................	2,456,000	2.25	3.00	3.75	7.75
1851........................	200,750	7.00	11.00	17.50	35.00
1851O......................	402,000	2.00	2.75	3.50	7.50
1852........................	77,130	14.00	19.00	30.00	70.00
1852O......................	144,000	10.00	14.00	18.00	35.00
1853O No arrows or rays. (Ex. rare)					
Beware 1858-O altered date.....		—	—	—	—

Variety 2
Arrows at date,
rays around eagle
1853 only

1853........................	3,532,708	4.00	6.00	10.00	17.50
1853O......................	1,328,000	4.50	7.00	12.00	20.00

Variety 3 — Arrows at date, no rays 1854-1855

1854........................	2,982,000	2.00	3.50	4.50	7.00
1854O......................	5,240,000	2.00	3.50	4.50	7.00
1855........................	759,500	2.50	4.00	6.00	8.00
1855O......................	3,688,000	2.00	3.50	4.50	7.00
1855S......................	129,950	17.00	27.50	45.00	95.00

Variety 1 resumed 1856-1866

1856........................	938,000	2.00	2.75	3.50	5.00
1856O......................	2,658,000	2.00	2.75	3.50	5.00
1856S......................	211,000	5.50	8.00	12.50	37.50

HALF DOLLARS

	Quan. Minted	Good	V. Good	Fine	V. Fine
1857	1,988,000	$ 2.00	$ 2.75	$ 3.50	$ 5.00
1857O	818,000	2.00	2.75	3.75	5.00
1857S	158,000	8.00	11.00	17.50	37.50
1858	4,226,000	2.00	2.75	3.50	5.00
1858O	7,294,000	2.00	2.75	3.50	5.00
1858S	476,000	3.00	5.50	9.50	16.00
1859	748,000	2.00	2.75	3.50	5.00
1859O	2,834,000	2.00	2.75	3.50	5.00
1859S	566,000	3.50	6.00	10.00	16.00
1860	303,700	2.00	2.75	3.50	5.00
1860O	1,290,000	2.00	2.75	3.50	5.00
1860S	472,000	2.50	3.50	5.00	9.00
1861	2,888,400	2.00	2.75	3.50	5.00
1861O*	2,532,633	2.00	2.75	3.50	6.00
1861 Confederate reverse (restrike)	....				200.00
1861S	939,500	2.00	3.00	4.00	7.00
1862	253,550	2.00	2.75	3.50	5.00
1862S	1,352,000	2.00	2.75	3.75	6.50
1863	503,660	2.00	2.75	3.75	6.50
1863S	916,000	2.00	2.75	3.75	6.50
1864	379,570	2.00	2.75	3.75	6.50
1864S	658,000	2.00	2.75	3.75	6.50
1865	511,900	2.00	2.75	3.75	6.50
1865S	675,000	2.00	2.75	3.75	6.50
1866S No motto. All kinds	1,054,000	20.00	30.00	50.00	95.00

*The 1861O quantity includes 330,000 struck under the United States government; 1,240,000 for the State of Louisiana after it seceded from the Union; and 962,633 after Louisiana joined the Confederate States of America. As all these 1861O coins were struck from U.S. dies it is impossible to distinguish one from another. They should not be confused with the very rare Confederate half dollar of 1861, which has a distinctive reverse.

Variety 4 —
Motto "In God We Trust"
added above eagle 1866-1873

1866	745,625	2.50	3.25	4.25	7.00
1866S With motto		2.50	3.25	4.25	7.50
1867	449,925	2.00	2.75	3.75	6.50
1867S	1,196,000	2.00	2.75	3.50	5.50
1868	418,200	2.00	2.75	3.75	6.00
1868S	1,160,000	2.00	2.75	3.50	5.50
1869	795,900	2.00	2.75	3.50	5.50
1869S	656,000	2.00	2.75	3.50	5.50
1870	634,900	2.00	2.75	3.50	5.50
1870CC	54,617	25.00	35.00	55.00	110.00
1870S	1,004,000	2.00	2.75	3.75	9.00
1871	1,204,560	2.00	2.75	3.50	5.50
1871CC	139,950	20.00	32.50	50.00	100.00
1871S	2,178,000	2.00	2.75	3.75	5.50

HALF DOLLARS

	Quan. Minted	Good	V. Good	Fine	V. Fine
1872	881,550	$ 2.00	$ 2.75	$ 3.75	$ 5.00
1872CC	272,000	15.00	22.50	37.50	60.00
1872S	580,000	2.25	2.75	4.00	8.50
1873 No arrows	801,800	2.00	2.75	3.75	6.50
1873CC No arrows	122,500	15.00	25.00	45.00	65.00
1873S No arrows	5,000	Unknown in any collection.			

Variety 5 — Arrows at date 1873-1874

1873 Arrows at date	1,815,700	7.00	10.00	16.00	25.00
1873CC Arrows	214,560	10.00	15.00	25.00	37.50
1873S Arrows	228,000	9.00	14.00	20.00	30.00
1874 Arrows	2,360,300	6.50	12.00	16.00	25.00
1874CC Arrows	59,000	17.50	27.50	45.00	85.00
1874S Arrows	394,000	11.00	16.00	25.00	40.00

Variety 4 resumed 1875-1891

1875	6,027,500	2.00	2.75	3.50	5.00
1875CC	1,008,000	2.50	3.50	5.50	11.00
1875S	3,200,000	2.00	2.75	3.50	5.00
1876	8,419,150	2.00	2.75	3.50	5.00
1876CC	1,956,000	2.50	3.50	5.50	8.00
1876S	4,528,000	2.00	2.75	3.50	5.00
1877	8,304,510	2.00	2.75	3.50	5.00
1877CC	1,420,000	2.50	3.25	4.50	9.00
1877S	5,356,000	2.00	2.75	3.50	5.00
1878	1,378,400	2.00	2.75	3.50	5.00
1878CC	62,000	40.00	50.00	70.00	120.00
1878S	12,000	150.00	200.00	300.00	600.00
1879	5,900	20.00	22.50	27.50	30.00
1880	9,755	17.00	20.00	24.00	27.50
1881	10,975	17.00	20.00	24.00	27.50
1882	5,500	20.00	22.50	27.50	30.00
1883	9,039	17.00	20.00	22.50	27.50
1884	5,275	17.00	20.00	22.50	27.50
1885	6,130	17.00	20.00	22.50	27.50
1886	5,886	32.50	35.00	37.50	40.00
1887	5,710	20.00	22.50	25.00	30.00
1888	12,833	17.00	20.00	22.50	25.00
1889	12,711	17.00	20.00	22.50	25.00
1890	12,590	20.00	22.50	25.00	27.00
1891	200,600	2.50	3.25	4.25	6.50

BARBER or LIBERTY HEAD TYPE 1892-1915

GOOD—*Date and legends readable. LIBERTY worn off headband.*

FINE—*LIBERTY completely readable, but not sharp.*

V. FINE—*All letters in LIBERTY evenly plain.*

[69]

HALF DOLLARS

Quan. Minted	Gd.	Fine	V.F.
1892.....935,245	$1.75	$4.00	$7.75
1892O....390,000	11.00	20.00	30.00
1892S...1,029,028	11.50	21.00	34.00
1893....1,826,792	1.25	3.25	7.00
1893O...1,389,000	2.75	6.00	11.50
1893S....740,000	11.50	19.00	27.50
1894....1,148,972	1.90	4.00	8.00
1894O..2,138,000	2.25	6.00	12.50
1894S...4,048,690	2.00	5.75	12.00
1895....1,835,218	1.25	3.25	7.00
1895O...1,766,000	1.75	5.00	8.50
1895S...1,108,086	2.50	7.00	13.00
1896.....950,762	2.00	4.25	9.00
1896O....924,000	3.00	7.50	20.00
1896S...1,140,948	11.50	23.00	37.50
1897....2,480,731	.90	2.50	6.00
1897O...632,000	11.00	21.00	30.00
1897S...933,900	11.00	21.00	30.00
1898....2,956,735	.90	2.50	6.00
1898O....874,000	2.25	4.50	8.00
1898S...2,358,550	1.75	4.25	8.00
1899....5,538,846	.90	2.50	6.00
1899O...1,724,000	1.50	4.00	7.50
1899S...1,686,411	1.50	4.00	7.50
1900....4,762,912	.90	2.50	6.00
1900O...2,744,000	1.25	4.00	8.50
1900S...2,560,322	1.25	4.00	8.50
1901....4,268,813	.90	2.50	6.00
1901O...1,124,000	2.00	6.00	19.00
1901S....847,044	4.50	22.50	45.00
1902....4,922,777	.90	2.50	6.00
1902O...2,526,000	1.25	3.00	8.00
1902S...1,460,670	1.50	4.75	14.00
1903....2,278,755	.90	2.50	6.00
1903O...2,100,000	1.00	4.00	11.50
1903S...1,920,772	1.50	4.75	15.00
1904....2,992,670	.90	2.50	6.00

Quan. Minted	Gd.	Fine	V.F.
1904O...1,117,600	$1.25	$4.00	$9.50
1904S....553,038	3.75	11.00	23.50
1905.....662,727	2.00	4.75	10.00
1905O....505,000	2.50	7.00	12.50
1905S...2,494,000	1.00	3.00	7.75
1906....2,638,675	.90	2.50	6.00
1906D..4,028,000	.90	2.50	6.00
1906O...2,446,000	1.15	3.50	8.00
1906S...1,740,154	1.15	3.50	8.00
1907....2,598,575	.90	2.50	6.00
1907D..3,856,000	.90	2.50	6.00
1907O...3,946,600	.90	2.50	6.00
1907S...1,250,000	1.00	3.50	7.50
1908....1,354,545	.90	2.50	6.50
1908D..3,280,000	.90	2.50	6.00
1908O..5,360,000	.90	2.50	6.00
1908S...1,644,828	1.25	3.75	8.25
1909....2,368,650	.90	2.50	6.00
1909O...925,400	1.75	3.50	8.00
1909S...1,764,000	1.00	3.00	6.50
1910.....418,551	2.25	5.00	9.00
1910S...1,948,000	1.00	3.00	6.50
1911...1,406,543	.90	2.50	6.00
1911D....695,080	1.75	4.00	7.50
1911S...1,272,000	1.00	3.00	6.50
1912....1,550,700	.90	2.50	6.00
1912D..2,300,800	.90	2.50	6.00
1912S...1,370,000	.90	2.50	6.00
1913.....188,627	7.00	14.00	20.00
1913D....534,000	1.50	4.00	8.00
1913S....604,000	1.75	4.25	10.00
1914.....124,610	9.00	20.00	31.00
1914S....992,000	1.25	3.50	8.00
1915.....138,450	8.00	16.00	25.00
1915D..1,170,400	.90	2.50	6.00
1915S...1,604,000	.90	2.75	6.25

LIBERTY WALKING TYPE 1916-1947

GOOD—Most of IN GOD WE TRUST is visible.

V. GOOD—Motto is distinct. About half of skirt lines at left are clear.

FINE—All skirt lines evident, but worn in spots. Details in sandal below motto are clear.

V. FINE—Lines on skirt incomplete. Lines in sandal complete but not bold. Some wear on breast and arm.

HALF DOLLARS

Proof totals shown in parentheses.

	Quan. Minted	Good	V. Good	Fine	V. Fine
1916	608,000	$ 4.50	$ 6.00	$ 9.00	$12.00
1916D on obv.	1,014,400	3.25	4.75	6.75	10.00
1916S on obv.	508,000	10.75	15.00	21.00	30.00
1917	12,292,000	.60	.85	1.10	2.50
1917D on obv.	765,400	3.25	4.00	7.75	13.75
1917D on rev.	1,940,000	1.00	1.75	4.00	10.00
1917S on obv.	952,000	3.25	6.00	15.00	32.50
1917S on rev.	5,554,000	.75	1.00	1.75	4.25
1918	6,634,000	.65	.85	1.65	5.00
1918D	3,853,040	.65	1.00	2.25	7.50
1918S	10,282,000	.65	1.00	1.75	4.75
1919	962,000	2.00	3.00	5.00	11.00
1919D	1,165,000	1.75	3.00	6.00	22.00
1919S	1,552,000	1.50	2.75	6.25	24.00
1920	6,372,000	.65	.80	1.25	3.00
1920D	1,551,000	1.00	1.50	3.00	10.00
1920S	4,624,000	.85	1.25	2.50	8.50
1921	246,000	19.00	22.50	32.50	52.50
1921D	208,000	34.00	40.00	46.00	75.00
1921S	548,000	4.50	6.75	14.00	27.50
1923S	2,178,000	.80	1.00	2.25	12.50
1927S	2,392,000	.70	1.00	1.60	3.50
1928S	1,940,000	.70	1.00	1.60	3.50
1929D	1,001,200	1.00	1.50	2.10	3.85
1929S	1,902,000	.70	1.00	1.25	2.50
1933S	1,786,000	.85	1.10	1.35	2.75
1934	6,964,000			.70	.90
1934D	2,361,100		.65	.90	1.25
1934S	3,652,000		.65	.90	1.65
1935	9,162,000				.75
1935D	3,003,800		.65	.85	1.25
1935S	3,854,000		.65	.85	1.25
1936 (3,901)	12,617,901				.75
1936D	4,252,400				1.00
1936S	3,884,000			.65	1.00
1937 (5,728)	9,527,728				.75
1937D	1,760,001		1.25	1.50	2.50
1937S	2,090,000		.65	1.00	1.50
1938 (8,152)	4,118,152				.70
1938D	491,600	13.00	15.00	19.00	25.00
1939 (8,808)	6,820,808				.60
1939D	4,267,800				.65
1939S	2,552,000				.85
1940 (11,279)	9,167,279				.60
1940S	4,550,000				.60
1941 (15,412)	24,207,412				.60
1941D	11,248,400				.60
1941S	8,098,000				.60
1942 (21,120)	47,839,120				.60
1942D	10,973,800				.60
1942S	12,708,000				.60
1943	53,190,000				.60
1943D	11,346,000				.60

HALF DOLLARS

	Quan. Minted	Good	V. Good	Fine	V. Fine
1943S	13,450,000				$ .60
1944	28,206,000				.60
1944D	9,769,000				.60
1944S	8,904,000				.60
1945	31,502,000				.60
1945D	9,966,800				.60
1945S	10,156,000				.60
1946	12,118,000				.60
1946D	2,151,000	$ .60	$ .80	$1.00	1.25
1946S	3,724,000			.65	.85
1947	4,094,000				.80
1947D	3,900,600				.80

FRANKLIN TYPE 1948-1963

FINE—Initials JRS distinct and clearly separated.

V. FINE—Half of incused lines on bell must show.

EX. FINE—Wear spots appear at top of end curls and hair back of ears. On reverse, Liberty bell will show wear at top.

		Fine	V. F.	Ex. F.
1948	3,006,814	$2.00	$2.50	$2.75
1948D	4,028,600	.80	1.00	1.25
1949	5,714,000	1.00	1.15	1.35
1949D	4,120,600	.75	.90	1.25
1949S	3,744,000	.85	1.10	2.00
1950 (51,386)	7,793,509			.80
1950D	8,031,600			.80
1951 (57,500)	16,859,602			.75
1951D	9,475,200			.85
1951S	13,696,000		.75	1.00
1952 (81,980)	21,274,073			.70
1952D	25,395,600			.70
1952S	5,526,000		.75	1.00
1953 (128,800)	2,796,920	1.75	2.25	2.75
1953D	20,900,400			.70
1953S	4,148,000		.75	1.00
1954 (233,300)	13,421,503			.70
1954D	25,445,580			.70
1954S	4,993,400		.70	.95
1955 (378,200)	2,876,381	3.75	4.00	4.50
1956 (669,384)	4,701,384	.70	.85	1.00
1957 (1,247,952)	6,361,952			.60
1957D	19,966,850			.55
1958 (875,652)	4,917,652			.70
1958D	23,962,412			.55
1959 (1,149,291)	7,349,291			.55
1959D	13,053,750			.55

HALF DOLLARS

	Quan. Minted	Ex. Fine
1960 (1,691,602)	7,715,602	$ .55
1960D	18,215,812	.55
1961 (3,028,244)	8,290,000	.55
1961D	20,276,442	.55
1962 (3,218,019)	12,932,019	.55
1962D	35,473,281	.55
1963 (3,075,645)	25,239,645	.55
1963D	67,069,292	.55

KENNEDY TYPE 1964 to Date

Gilroy Roberts, former Chief Sculptor of the Mint, designed the obverse of this coin. His stylized initials are on the truncation of the forceful bust of President John F. Kennedy. The reverse, which uses the Presidential Coat of Arms for the motif, is the work of Frank Gasparro, now Head Engraver at the Mint.

		Ex. Fine
SILVER		
1964 (3,950,762)	277,254,766	$ .55
1964D	156,205,446	.55
SILVER CLAD		
1965	65,879,366	.55
1966	108,984,932	.50
1967	295,046,978	.50
1968D	246,951,930	.50
1968S Proof only	3,041,509	2.25

		Ex. Fine
1969D	129,881,800	$ .50
1969S Proof only	2,934,631	2.00
1970D	2,150,000	4.00
1970S Proof only	2,632,810	2.50
COPPER-NICKEL CLAD		
1971		.50
1971D		.50
1971S Proof only		2.00

SILVER DOLLARS

Major types of silver dollars are few, although the early dates are plentiful in die varieties. The first date, 1794, is quite rare. The bust type was adopted in the latter part of 1795 and all dates of this type are fairly common except one — the famous 1804. The 1804 silver dollar has been the most discussed coin in American numismatics. There are those that are called "originals" of which eight specimens are known, and those called "restrikes" of which seven specimens are known. Fake 1804's have been made by altering 1801's which are of the same general type; some of these altered dates are very cleverly done and almost defy detection.

Silver dollars of 1836, 1838 and 1839 are patterns. About 1,000 pieces of the common type 1836 were struck; of the other varieties only 3 to 18 were struck.

After 1840 all silver dollars are relatively available with exception of just a few dates, 1851, 1852, 1858, etc.

SILVER DOLLARS
FLOWING HAIR TYPE 1794-1795

FAIR—*Clear enough to identify.*
GOOD—*Date and letters readable. Main devices outlined, but lack details.*
V. GOOD—*Major details discernible. Letters well formed but worn.*
FINE—*Hair ends distinguishable. Top hairlines show, but otherwise worn smooth.*
V. FINE—*Hair in center shows some detail. Other details more bold.*

	Quan. Minted	Fair	Good	V. Good	Fine	V. Fine
1794	1,758	$435.00	$775.00	$1300.00	$2000.00	$3600.00
1795 All kinds	203,033	60.00	105.00	135.00	160.00	250.00

DRAPED BUST TYPE, SMALL EAGLE REVERSE 1795-1798

FAIR—*Clear enough to identify.*
GOOD—*Bust outlined, no detail. Date readable, some leaves evident.*
V. GOOD—*Drapery worn except deepest folds. Hairlines smooth.*
FINE—*All drapery lines distinguishable. Hairlines near cheek and neck show some detail.*
V. FINE—*Left side of drapery worn smooth.*

1795 Bust type		60.00	90.00	115.00	155.00	225.00
1796	72,920	47.50	65.00	95.00	130.00	200.00
1797	7,776	50.00	85.00	115.00	170.00	265.00
1798 15 stars	327,536	52.50	75.00	97.50	135.00	220.00
13 stars		50.00	72.50	90.00	130.00	200.00

SILVER DOLLARS
DRAPED BUST TYPE, HERALDIC EAGLE REVERSE 1798-1804

GOOD—Letters and date readable. E PLURIBUS UNUM obliterated.
V. GOOD—Motto partially readable. Only deepest drapery details visible. All other lines smooth.
FINE—All drapery lines distinguishable. Hairlines near cheek and neck show some detail.
V. FINE—Left side of drapery worn smooth.

	Quan. Minted	Good	V. Good	Fine	V. Fine
1798 Heraldic eagle		$52.50	$70.00	$95.00	$125.00
1799	423,515	50.00	72.50	90.00	120.00
1800	220,920	50.00	72.50	90.00	120.00
1801	54,454	50.00	72.50	90.00	120.00
1802	41,650	50.00	72.50	90.00	120.00
1803	85,634	50.00	72.50	90.00	120.00
1804 Variety 1, letter O in "OF" above cloud				Proof	$25,000.00
Variety 2, letter O above space between clouds				Proof	25,000.00

PATTERN SILVER DOLLARS

Owing to the interest in pattern silver dollars of 1836, 1838 and 1839 we are including a list of them with the dollars of regular issue. There was no regular issue of dollars 1805 to 1839 inclusive. The figures given for the following three years are approximate, as restrikes of many varieties are known to have been made. There are several other minor varieties of the 1836-1839 series, all extremely rare and seldom available.

	Quan. Minted	V. Fine	Proof
1836 Obv. with name on base. Rev. with stars.			
Plain edge. (shown above)	1,000	$450.00	$1000.00
1838 Obv. without name, stars added around border.			
Rev. with stars. Reeded edge	25		1500.00
1839 Rev. without stars, reeded edge	300	500.00	1500.00

[75]

SILVER DOLLARS

LIBERTY SEATED TYPE — Regular Issues 1840-1873

Variety 1 — No motto above eagle 1840-1865

V. GOOD—*Any three letters of LIBERTY should be at least two-thirds complete.*

FINE—*All drapery lines show but partly worn. Hair from brow, over ear and down neck, well outlined but shows only slight detail.*

V. FINE—*LIBERTY is strong and its ribbon shows slight wear.*

	Quan. Minted	V. Good	Fine	V. Fine
1840	61,005	$17.50	$23.50	$32.50
1841	173,000	15.00	17.50	24.00
1842	184,618	15.00	17.50	24.00
1843	165,100	15.00	17.50	24.00
1844	20,000	22.50	35.00	45.00
1845	24,500	22.50	35.00	45.00
1846	110,600	15.00	17.50	24.00
1846O	59,000	15.00	20.00	27.50
1847	140,750	15.00	17.50	24.00
1848	15,000	27.50	37.50	47.50
1849	62,600	15.00	17.50	24.00
1850	7,500	35.00	50.00	75.00
1850O	40,000	16.00	21.00	30.00
1851 (Original)	1,300			450.00
1852 (Original)	1,100		Unc.	1325.00
1853	46,110	25.00	35.00	50.00
1854	33,140	37.50	60.00	80.00
1855	26,000	45.00	65.00	90.00
1856	63,500	23.00	32.50	50.00
1857	94,000	22.50	31.00	45.00
1858 (Not in Mint Director's report)	Est. 80		Proof	1150.00
1859	256,500	15.00	20.00	27.50
1859O	360,000	15.00	17.50	24.00
1859S	20,000	24.00	32.50	45.00
1860	218,930	15.00	18.00	25.00
1860O	515,000	15.00	17.50	22.50
1861	78,500	19.00	25.00	35.00
1862	12,090	20.00	28.00	42.00
1863	27,660	20.00	28.00	38.00
1864	31,170	20.00	28.00	38.00
1865	47,000	18.00	24.00	34.00

SILVER DOLLARS

Variety 2 —
Motto "In God We Trust"
added above eagle 1866-1873

	Quan. Minted	V. Good	Fine	V. Fine
1866 With motto	49,625	$19.00	$24.00	$37.50
1867	47,525	19.00	24.00	37.50
1868	162,700	15.00	19.00	30.00
1869	424,300	15.00	17.50	22.50
1870	416,000	15.00	17.50	22.50
1870CC	12,462	36.00	57.50	72.50
1870S	—			
1871	1,074,760	15.00	17.50	20.00
1871CC	1,376	225.00	300.00	450.00
1872	1,106,450	15.00	17.50	20.00
1872CC	3,150	110.00	150.00	200.00
1872S	9,000	27.50	42.50	57.50
1873	293,600	15.00	17.50	20.00
1873CC	2,300	300.00	425.00	600.00
1873S	700	Unknown in any collection		

LIBERTY HEAD or MORGAN TYPE 1878-1921

George T. Morgan designed the silver dollar which was first issued in 1878. This type is sometimes known as the "Bland" dollar, after Richard P. Bland, co-author of the Bland Silver Bill of 1878 which provided for the new design.

270,232,722 silver dollars were melted under the Pittman Act of April, 1918, which probably accounts for the scarcity of some dates.

V. FINE—*Two-thirds of hairlines from top of forehead to ear must show. Ear well defined. Feathers on eagle's breast worn at center.*

EX. FINE—*All hairlines strong and ear bold. Eagle's feathers all plain but slight wear on breast and wing tips.*

	Quan. Minted	V. Good	Fine	V. Fine
1878 8 tail feathers	} 10,509,550	3.00	3.50	8.50
1878 7 tail feathers		2.15	2.40	3.50
1878CC	2,212,000	3.00	4.00	9.00
1878S	9,774,000	2.15	2.40	3.00
1879	14,807,100	2.15	2.40	3.00
1879CC	756,000	12.50	23.00	130.00
1879O	2,887,000	2.15	2.40	3.50
1879S	9,110,000	2.15	2.40	3.00
1880	12,601,355	2.15	2.40	3.00
1880CC	591,000	16.00	25.00	40.00

SILVER DOLLARS

	Quan. Minted	V. Fine	Ex. Fine	Unc.
1880O	5,305,000	$ 2.15	$ 2.40	$ 3.50
1880S	8,900,000	2.15	2.40	3.00
1881	9,163,975	2.15	2.40	3.00
1881CC	296,000	30.00	35.00	45.00
1881O	5,708,000	2.15	2.40	3.00
1881S	12,760,000	2.15	2.40	3.00
1882	11,101,000	2.15	2.40	3.00
1882CC	1,133,000	7.50	10.00	20.00
1882O	6,090,000	2.15	2.40	3.00
1882S	9,250,000	2.15	2.40	3.00
1883	12,291,039	2.15	2.40	3.00
1883CC	1,204,000	7.50	10.00	17.50
1883O	8,725,000	2.15	2.40	3.00
1883S	6,250,000	2.25	3.50	19.00
1884	14,070,875	2.15	2.40	3.00
1884CC	1,136,000	13.00	15.00	23.00
1884O	9,730,000	2.15	2.40	3.00
1884S	3,200,000	2.50	3.75	40.00
1885	17,787,767	2.15	2.40	3.00
1885CC	228,000	27.50	34.00	42.00
1885O	9,185,000	2.15	2.40	3.00
1885S	1,497,000	2.25	3.00	7.50
1886	19,963,886	2.15	2.40	3.00
1886O	10,710,000	2.25	3.00	9.25
1886S	750,000	6.50	10.00	23.00
1887	20,290,710	2.15	2.40	3.00
1887O	11,550,000	2.15	2.40	3.50
1887S	1,771,000	3.00	4.25	8.50
1888	19,183,833	2.15	2.40	3.00
1888O	12,150,000	2.15	2.40	3.00
1888S	657,000	10.00	12.50	20.00
1889	21,726,811	2.15	2.40	3.00
1889CC	350,000	50.00	110.00	500.00
1889O	11,875,000	2.25	2.75	7.00
1889S	700,000	9.50	12.50	20.00
1890	16,802,590	2.15	2.40	3.00
1890CC	2,309,041	4.00	6.50	18.00
1890O	10,701,000	2.15	2.40	6.00
1890S	8,230,373	2.15	2.40	5.00
1891	8,694,206	2.25	3.00	6.25
1891CC	1,618,000	4.00	6.50	16.00
1891O	7,954,529	2.15	2.50	7.00
1891S	5,296,000	2.15	3.00	6.50
1892	1,037,245	2.25	3.00	15.00
1892CC	1,352,000	11.00	17.50	40.00
1892O	2,744,000	2.15	3.50	11.00
1892S	1,200,000	6.00	16.00	850.00
1893	378,792	6.00	8.00	35.00
1893CC	677,000	14.00	30.00	140.00
1893O	300,000	11.00	22.50	110.00
1893S	100,000	140.00	250.00	2750.00
1894	110,972	30.00	45.00	125.00
1894O	1,723,000	2.75	5.50	35.00
1894S	1,260,000	5.00	11.00	30.00

SILVER DOLLARS

	Quan. Minted	V. Fine	Ex. Fine	Unc.
1895 (Beware removed mint mark)......12,880			Proof	$3000.00
1895O.............................450,000	$10.00	$19.00	200.00
1895S.............................400,000	21.00	50.00	300.00
1896...........................9,976,762	2.15	2.40	3.00
1896O...........................4,900,000	2.50	4.00	30.00
1896S...........................5,000,000	6.00	20.00	130.00
1897...........................2,822,731	2.25	2.50	4.00
1897O...........................4,004,000	2.50	3.75	22.50
1897S...........................5,825,000	2.25	2.50	6.00
1898...........................5,884,735	2.15	2.40	3.00
1898O...........................4,440,000	2.15	2.40	3.25
1898S...........................4,102,000	2.50	4.50	17.50
1899.............................330,846	6.00	8.00	15.00
1899O..........................12,290,000	2.15	2.40	3.00
1899S...........................2,562,000	3.00	5.00	22.00
1900...........................8,830,912	2.15	2.40	3.00
1900O..........................12,590,000	2.15	2.40	3.00
1900S...........................3,540,000	2.75	4.50	16.00
1901...........................6,962,813	4.00	7.00	45.00
1901O..........................13,320,000	2.15	2.40	3.00
1901S...........................2,284,000	3.00	4.75	25.00
1902...........................7,994,777	2.50	2.75	4.50
1902O...........................8,636,000	2.15	2.40	3.00
1902S...........................1,530,000	14.00	22.00	50.00
1903...........................4,652,755	2.50	2.75	4.50
1903O...........................4,450,000	10.00	16.00	24.00
1903S...........................1,241,000	7.00	15.00	215.00
1904...........................2,788,650	3.00	5.00	10.00
1904O...........................3,720,000	2.15	2.40	3.00
1904S...........................2,304,000	4.25	10.50	120.00
1921..........................44,690,000	2.15	2.40	2.90
1921D.........................20,345,000	2.15	2.40	3.00
1921S.........................21,695,000	2.15	2.40	3.00

PEACE TYPE 1921-1935

Agitation for a coin to commemorate the coming of peace after World War I started during the 1920 American Numismatic Association convention. A special committee petitioned government authorities to produce such a coin. A half dollar was under consideration for a time, but the silver dollar afforded a better opportunity for art effect than a smaller coin. Anthony de Francisci designed the new dollar, which was placed in circulation as a regular issue on January 3, 1922.

SILVER DOLLARS

V. FINE—Hair over eye well worn. Some strands over ear well defined. Some eagle feathers on top and outside edge of right wing will show.

EX. FINE—Hairlines over brow and ear are strong though slightly worn. Outside wing feathers at right and those at top are visible but faint.

	Quan. Minted	V. Fine	Ex. Fine	Unc.
1921 Peace type	1,006,473	$7.00	$9.00	$21.00
1922	51,737,000	2.15	2.40	2.90
1922D	15,063,000	2.15	2.40	3.00
1922S	17,475,000	2.15	2.40	3.00
1923	30,800,000	2.15	2.40	2.90
1923D	6,811,000	2.15	2.40	6.00
1923S	19,020,000	2.15	2.40	3.25
1924	11,811,000	2.15	2.40	3.00
1924S	1,728,000	3.00	4.75	22.50
1925	10,198,000	2.15	2.40	2.90
1925S	1,610,000	2.50	3.50	9.00
1926	1,939,000	2.25	3.50	6.50
1926D	2,348,700	2.25	3.00	6.50
1926S	6,980,000	2.15	2.40	4.50
1927	848,000	6.00	8.50	18.50
1927D	1,268,900	3.50	5.00	21.00
1927S	866,000	3.50	6.00	23.00
1928	360,649	37.50	45.00	65.00
1928S	1,632,000	2.50	3.50	15.00
1934	954,057	5.00	7.00	13.00
1934D	1,569,500	3.25	5.00	19.50
1934S	1,011,000	6.00	19.00	125.00
1935	1,576,000	2.50	4.50	8.50
1935S	1,964,000	2.50	6.50	25.00

EISENHOWER DOLLAR 1971

Intended to honor both the late President Dwight D. Eisenhower and the first landing of man on the moon, this design is the work of mint engraver Frank Gasparro, whose initials are on the truncation and below the eagle. The reverse is an adaptation of the official Apollo 11 insignia. Collectors' coins were struck in 40% silver composition and the circulation issue in copper-nickel. Mint mark location is above the date.

	Unc.
1971 Copper-nickel clad	$1.00
1971D Copper-nickel clad	1.00
1971S Silver clad	3.00

TRADE DOLLARS
(Coined from 1873 to 1885)

This coin was issued for circulation in the Orient to compete with the Mexican peso. When first coined they were legal tender in United States to the extent of $5.00 but with the decline in price of silver bullion Congress repealed the legal tender provision in 1876 and authorized the Treasury to limit coinage to export demand. In 1887 a law was passed authorizing the Treasury to redeem all Trade dollars which were not mutilated. U.S. Trade dollars are no longer circulating in the Orient. Those struck in the last few years of coinage were undoubtedly all proofs to satisfy collectors' demands.

The Trade dollars of 1884 and 1885 were unknown to collectors generally until 1908. None is listed in the Director's report. The law authorizing Trade dollars was repealed in February, 1887.

FINE—Mottoes and LIBERTY readable but worn.
EX. FINE—Mottoes and LIBERTY are sharp. Only slight wear on rims.

	Quan. Minted	Fine	Ex. Fine	Proof
1873	397,500	$20.00	$33.00	
1873CC	124,500	27.50	57.50	
1873S	703,000	20.00	35.00	
1874	987,800	16.00	22.00	
1874CC	1,373,200	25.00	42.50	
1874S	2,549,000	20.00	33.00	
1875	218,900	22.50	40.00	
1875CC	1,573,700	22.50	40.00	
1875S	4,487,000	16.00	22.00	
1876	456,150	17.00	25.00	
1876CC	509,000	25.00	45.00	
1876S	5,227,000	16.00	22.00	
1877	3,039,710	16.00	22.00	
1877CC	534,000	35.00	55.00	
1877S	9,519,000	16.00	22.00	
1878	900			$ 250.00
1878CC	97,000	87.50	140.00	
1878S	4,162,000	16.00	22.00	
1879	1,541			235.00
1880	1,987			225.00
1881	960			240.00
1882	1,097			235.00
1883	979			265.00
1884	10			5000.00
1885	5			7500.00

GOLD DOLLARS

Coinage of the gold dollar was begun in 1849; those coined 1849 to 1854 are known as the Liberty head or small sized type. In 1854 the piece was made larger in diameter and thinner and the design was changed to a feather headdress on a female, popularly known as the Indian head type or large size gold dollar (1854 was coined in both types). In 1856 the type was changed slightly by enlarging the size of the head.

Values for gold given in this handbook are for coins in "very good" or better condition. Dealers do not purchase gold coins on a bullion basis, therefore there is no numismatic market for gold in less than V. Good condition.

LIBERTY HEAD TYPE, 1849-1854

V. GOOD—*Partial LIBERTY on headband will show.*

FINE—*Full LIBERTY on headband. All hairlines and beads worn smooth.*

EX. FINE—*Little wear on hair, knobs on coronet must be bold.*

	Quan. Minted	V. Good	Fine	Ex. Fine
1849	688,567	$22.50	$27.50	$40.00
1849C	11,634	35.00	60.00	90.00
1849D	21,588	35.00	55.00	120.00
1849O	215,000	22.50	27.50	40.00
1850	481,953	22.50	27.50	40.00
1850C	6,966	45.00	80.00	140.00
1850D	8,382	40.00	60.00	95.00
1850O	14,000	22.50	27.50	40.00
1851	3,317,671	22.50	27.50	40.00
1851C	41,267	30.00	50.00	90.00
1851D	9,882	35.00	60.00	100.00
1851O	290,000	22.50	27.50	40.00
1852	2,045,351	22.50	27.50	40.00
1852C	9,434	45.00	75.00	110.00
1852D	6,360	50.00	80.00	115.00
1852O	140,000	22.50	27.50	40.00
1853	4,076,051	22.50	27.50	40.00
1853C	11,515	35.00	60.00	80.00
1853D	6,583	40.00	65.00	110.00
1853O	290,000	22.50	27.50	40.00
1854	736,709	22.50	27.50	40.00
1854D	2,935	60.00	125.00	175.00
1854S	14,632	25.00	45.00	75.00

INDIAN HEAD TYPE, Small head 1854-1856

V. GOOD—*Feathers and headdress considerably worn.*

FINE—*Tips of feather curls on headdress partially worn away.*

EX. FINE—*Slight wear on headdress feather curls.*

1854	902,736	40.00	60.00	125.00
1855	758,269	40.00	60.00	125.00
1855C	9,803	45.00	85.00	160.00
1855D	1,811	250.00	475.00	750.00
1855O	55,000	40.00	60.00	125.00
1856S	24,600	45.00	65.00	130.00

GOLD DOLLARS
INDIAN HEAD TYPE, Large head 1856-1889

V. GOOD—At least 3 letters show in LIBERTY.

FINE—Full LIBERTY in headband. Beads partially worn. Curled feathers worn flat.

EX. FINE—Trace of wear above and right of eye and on curled feathers.

	Quan. Minted	V. Good	Fine	Ex. Fine
1856	1,762,936	$25.00	$30.00	$42.50
1856D	1,460	200.00	450.00	800.00
1857	774,789	25.00	30.00	42.50
1857C	13,280	35.00	65.00	100.00
1857D	3,533	60.00	130.00	225.00
1857S	10,000	30.00	37.50	65.00
1858	117,995	25.00	30.00	42.50
1858D	3,477	90.00	185.00	375.00
1858S	10,000	30.00	45.00	65.00
1859	168,244	25.00	30.00	42.50
1859C	5,235	45.00	85.00	135.00
1859D	4,952	45.00	95.00	150.00
1859S	15,000	27.50	37.50	75.00
1860	36,668	25.00	30.00	42.50
1860D	1,566	350.00	625.00	1450.00
1860S	13,000	30.00	40.00	70.00
1861	527,499	25.00	30.00	42.50
1861D		650.00	1450.00	2200.00
1862	1,361,390	25.00	30.00	42.50
1863	6,250	45.00	85.00	150.00
1864	5,950	35.00	55.00	90.00
1865	3,725	40.00	80.00	125.00
1866	7,130	30.00	50.00	85.00
1867	5,250	35.00	60.00	85.00
1868	10,525	30.00	40.00	70.00
1869	5,925	30.00	50.00	85.00
1870	6,335	30.00	40.00	70.00
1870S	3,000	90.00	180.00	225.00
1871	3,930	30.00	40.00	65.00
1872	3,530	30.00	40.00	65.00
1873	125,125	25.00	30.00	42.50
1874	198,820	25.00	30.00	42.50
1875	420	250.00	400.00	600.00
1876	3,245	30.00	40.00	65.00
1877	3,920	30.00	45.00	70.00
1878	3,020	30.00	40.00	65.00
1879	3,030	30.00	40.00	65.00
1880	1,636	35.00	50.00	85.00
1881	7,707	25.00	35.00	55.00
1882	5,125	25.00	35.00	55.00
1883	11,007	25.00	35.00	55.00
1884	6,236	25.00	32.50	50.00
1885	12,261	25.00	32.50	50.00
1886	6,016	25.00	32.50	50.00
1887	8,543	25.00	32.50	50.00
1888	16,580	25.00	30.00	45.00
1889	30,729	25.00	30.00	45.00

QUARTER EAGLES ($2.50 Gold Pieces)

Coinage began in 1796 and the last year is dated 1929. Most of the dates prior to 1834 are rare, some excessively rare; after 1834 only scattered dates are considered rare. One of these, 1848, has the letters **CAL** over the eagle in reference to California gold.

CAPPED BUST TO RIGHT 1796-1807

V. GOOD—*Liberty's hair smooth. Only partial motto E PLURIBUS UNUM.*

FINE—*Hair worn smooth on high spots. E PLURIBUS UNUM weak but readable.*

EX. FINE—*Slight wear on high spots.*

	Quan. Minted	V. Good	Fine	Ex. Fine
1796 No stars on obverse	963	$850.00	$1500.00	$3500.00

1796 With stars on obverse	432	850.00	1500.00	3500.00
1797	427	250.00	400.00	1050.00
1798	1,094	300.00	500.00	1100.00
1802 2 over 1	3,035	175.00	260.00	900.00
1804	3,327	160.00	285.00	750.00
1805	1,781	160.00	285.00	750.00
1806 6 over 4	} 1,616	175.00	410.00	1050.00
1806 6 over 5		175.00	310.00	600.00
1807	6,812	130.00	235.00	500.00

CAPPED BUST TO LEFT 1808-1834

V. GOOD—*Half of E PLURIBUS UNUM shows. Part of Liberty shows.*

FINE—*E PLURIBUS UNUM and LIBERTY on headband readable but weak.*

EX. FINE—*Motto and LIBERTY sharp. Liberty's hair only slightly worn.*

1808	2,710	300.00	750.00	2450.00
1821 Reduced Size	6,448	100.00	175.00	400.00
1824 4 over 1	2,600	100.00	175.00	425.00
1825	4,434	110.00	225.00	650.00
1826 6 over 5	760	110.00	225.00	650.00
1827	2,800	110.00	225.00	475.00
1829	3,403	100.00	200.00	450.00
1830	4,540	100.00	200.00	450.00
1831	4,520	100.00	200.00	450.00
1832	4,400	100.00	200.00	450.00
1833	4,160	100.00	200.00	450.00
1834 With motto above eagle	4,000	150.00	500.00	1000.00

QUARTER EAGLES ($2.50 Gold Pieces)

V. GOOD—*Partial LIBERTY.*

FINE—*LIBERTY readable and complete. Curl under ear outlined but no detail.*

EX. FINE—*Slight wear on hair at top of head, below "L" in LIBERTY, top of coronet and on reverse, upper wings and neck of eagle.*

	Quan. Minted	V. Good	Fine	Ex. Fine
1834 Without motto	112,234	$25.00	$40.00	$60.00
1835	131,402	25.00	40.00	60.00
1836	547,986	25.00	40.00	60.00
1837	45,080	25.00	40.00	60.00
1838	47,030	25.00	40.00	60.00
1838C	7,880	47.50	75.00	150.00
1839	27,021	25.00	40.00	60.00
1839C	18,140	40.00	65.00	115.00
1839D	13,674	45.00	70.00	135.00
1839O	17,781	25.00	45.00	75.00

CORONET HEAD TYPE 1840-1907

1840	18,859	20.00	24.00	32.50
1840C	12,822	20.00	30.00	65.00
1840D	3,532	25.00	50.00	85.00
1840O	33,580	20.00	24.00	32.50
1841 (Proofs only) Beware removed mint mark			Proof ———	
1841C	10,281	25.00	40.00	55.00
1841D	4,164	25.00	50.00	95.00
1842	2,823	25.00	45.00	75.00
1842C	6,729	22.50	40.00	55.00
1842D	4,643	22.50	40.00	65.00
1842O	19,800	20.00	24.00	32.50
1843	100,546	20.00	24.00	32.50
1843C Large or small date	26,064	20.00	35.00	50.00
1843D Small date	36,209	20.00	35.00	50.00
1843O Large date	76,000	20.00	24.00	32.50
1843O Small date	288,002	20.00	24.00	32.50
1844	6,784	20.00	30.00	65.00
1844C	11,622	20.00	35.00	50.00
1844D	17,332	20.00	35.00	50.00
1845	91,051	20.00	24.00	32.50
1845D	19,460	20.00	35.00	47.50
1845O		22.50	40.00	75.00
1846	21,598	20.00	24.00	32.50
1846C	4,808	22.50	40.00	85.00
1846D	19,303	20.00	32.50	60.00
1846O	66,000	20.00	24.00	32.50
1847	29,814	20.00	24.00	32.50
1847C	23,226	20.00	30.00	50.00
1847D	15,784	20.00	35.00	50.00

QUARTER EAGLES ($2.50 Gold Pieces)

CAL. above eagle on Reverse

CALIF. GOLD QUARTER EAGLE

In 1848 about two hundred and thirty ounces of gold were sent to Secretary of War Marcy by Col. R. B. Mason, Military Governor of California. The gold was turned over to the mint and made into quarter eagles. The distinguishing mark "CAL." was punched above the eagle on the reverse side, while the coins were in the die.

	Quan. Minted	V. Good	Fine	Ex. Fine
1847O	124,000	$20.00	$24.00	$32.50
1848	7,489	35.00	75.00	125.00
1848 CAL. over eagle	1,389	600.00	1100.00	1900.00
1848C	16,788	20.00	35.00	50.00
1848D	13,771	20.00	35.00	55.00
1849	23,294	20.00	24.00	32.50
1849C	10,220	20.00	40.00	57.50
1849D	10,945	20.00	40.00	65.00
1850	252,923	20.00	24.00	32.50
1850C	9,148	20.00	42.50	55.00
1850D	12,148	20.00	40.00	52.50
1850O	84,000	20.00	24.00	32.50
1851	1,372,748	20.00	24.00	32.50
1851C	14,923	20.00	40.00	60.00
1851D	11,264	20.00	40.00	70.00
1851O	148,000	20.00	24.00	32.50
1852	1,159,681	20.00	24.00	32.50
1852C	9,772	20.00	42.50	75.00
1852D	4,078	35.00	60.00	125.00
1852O	140,000	20.00	24.00	32.50
1853	1,404,668	20.00	24.00	32.50
1853D	3,178	40.00	90.00	150.00
1854	596,258	20.00	24.00	32.50
1854C	7,295	25.00	50.00	110.00
1854D	1,760	100.00	240.00	450.00
1854O	153,000	20.00	24.00	32.50
1854S	246	500.00	1250.00	2000.00
1855	235,480	20.00	24.00	32.50
1855C	3,677	30.00	60.00	85.00
1855D	1,123	65.00	210.00	375.00
1856	384,240	20.00	24.00	32.50
1856C	7,913	25.00	50.00	75.00
1856D	874	200.00	400.00	750.00
1856O	21,100	20.00	24.00	32.50
1856S	71,120	20.00	24.00	32.50
1857	214,130	20.00	24.00	32.50
1857D	2,364	30.00	60.00	95.00
1857O	34,000	20.00	24.00	32.50
1857S	69,200	20.00	24.00	32.50
1858	47,377	20.00	24.00	32.50
1858C	9,056	30.00	50.00	90.00
1859	39,444	20.00	24.00	32.50

QUARTER EAGLES ($2.50 Gold Pieces)

	Quan. Minted	V. Good	Fine	Ex. Fine
1859D	2,244	$45.00	$100.00	$175.00
1859S	15,200	20.00	24.00	32.50
1860	22,675	20.00	24.00	32.50
1860C	7,469	25.00	45.00	80.00
1860S	35,600	20.00	24.00	32.50
1861	1,283,878	20.00	24.00	32.50
1861S	24,000	20.00	24.00	32.50
1862	98,543	20.00	24.00	32.50
1862S	8,000	20.00	25.00	37.50
1863 (Proofs only) Beware removed mint mk...30			Proof	2500.00
1863S	10,800	20.00	25.00	40.00
1864	2,874	50.00	100.00	175.00
1865	1,545	60.00	110.00	225.00
1865S	23,376	20.00	24.00	32.50
1866	3,110	30.00	60.00	90.00
1866S	38,960	20.00	24.00	32.50
1867	3,250	20.00	30.00	42.50
1867S	28,000	20.00	24.00	35.00
1868	3,625	20.00	32.50	60.00
1868S	34,000	20.00	24.00	32.50
1869	4,345	20.00	27.50	45.00
1869S	29,500	20.00	24.00	32.50
1870	4,555	20.00	27.50	40.00
1870S	16,000	20.00	24.00	32.50
1871	5,350	20.00	25.00	40.00
1871S	22,000	20.00	24.00	32.50
1872	3,030	20.00	24.00	40.00
1872S	18,000	20.00	24.00	32.50
1873	178,025	20.00	24.00	32.50
1873S	27,000	20.00	24.00	32.50
1874	3,940	20.00	25.00	40.00
1875	420	100.00	200.00	325.00
1875S	11,600	20.00	24.00	35.00
1876	4,221	20.00	25.00	40.00
1876S	5,000	20.00	24.00	32.50
1877	1,652	22.50	40.00	75.00
1877S	35,400	20.00	24.00	32.50
1878	286,260	20.00	24.00	32.50
1878S	178,000	20.00	24.00	32.50
1879	88,990	20.00	24.00	32.50
1879S	43,500	20.00	24.00	32.50
1880	2,996	30.00	50.00	80.00
1881	691	75.00	125.00	225.00
1882	4,067	30.00	50.00	75.00
1883	2,002	30.00	50.00	100.00
1884	2,023	30.00	50.00	100.00
1885	887	75.00	125.00	225.00
1886	4,088	30.00	45.00	70.00
1887	6,282	25.00	40.00	60.00
1888	16,098	25.00	30.00	35.00
1889	17,648	25.00	30.00	35.00
1890	8,813	25.00	30.00	40.00
1891	11,040	25.00	30.00	35.00
1892	2,545	40.00	60.00	80.00

QUARTER EAGLES ($2.50 Gold Pieces)

	Quan. Minted	V. Good	Fine	Ex. Fine
1893	30,106	$22.50	$25.00	$35.00
1894	4,122	30.00	45.00	70.00
1895	6,119	27.50	37.50	55.00
1896	19,202	20.00	24.00	32.50
1897	29,904	20.00	24.00	32.50
1898	24,165	20.00	24.00	32.50
1899	27,350	20.00	24.00	32.50
1900	67,205	20.00	24.00	32.50
1901	91,323	20.00	24.00	32.50
1902	133,733	20.00	24.00	32.50
1903	201,257	20.00	24.00	32.50
1904	160,960	20.00	24.00	32.50
1905*	217,944	20.00	24.00	32.50
1906	176,490	20.00	24.00	32.50
1907	336,448	20.00	24.00	32.50

*Pieces dated 1905S are counterfeit.

INDIAN HEAD TYPE 1908-1929

V. GOOD—Outline of bonnet cord shows.

FINE—Knot in hair cord shows, but top feathers faint on wing.

EX. FINE—Cheekbone slightly worn. Warbonnet and headband feathers slightly worn.

1908	565,057	19.00	22.00	25.00
1909	441,899	19.00	22.00	25.00
1910	492,682	19.00	22.00	25.00
1911	704,191	19.00	22.00	25.00
1911D	55,680	75.00	125.00	200.00
1912	616,197	19.00	22.00	25.00
1913	722,165	19.00	22.00	25.00
1914	240,117	19.00	22.00	25.00
1914D	448,000	19.00	22.00	25.00
1915	606,100	19.00	22.00	25.00
1925D	578,000	19.00	22.00	25.00
1926	446,000	19.00	22.00	25.00
1927	388,000	19.00	22.00	25.00
1928	416,000	19.00	22.00	25.00
1929	532,000	19.00	22.00	25.00

THREE-DOLLAR GOLD PIECES

(Coined from 1854 to 1889)

Authorized to facilitate postal transactions when the letter rate was made 3-cents. The coin was very unpopular and was never circulated to any extent; and when the postal rate was changed from 3-cents the piece was discontinued.

All dates are of the same design; those struck in 1873, 1875 and 1876 are the rarest. Only 20 specimens were coined of the 1875 in proof condition. Mint records state that 25 pieces were coined of 1873, but more are known to exist; in fact they do not bring as much money as the 1876 of which 45 were reported coined.

THREE-DOLLAR GOLD PIECES

V. GOOD—At least 3 letters show in LIBERTY.

FINE—Details of curled feathers missing. Beads partly worn, but LIBERTY plain.

EX. FINE—Slight wear above and to right of eye, and tops of curled feathers.

	Quan. Minted	V. Good	Fine	Ex. Fine
1854	138,618	$ 65.00	$110.00	$165.00
1854D	1,120	250.00	450.00	900.00
1854O	24,000	65.00	110.00	165.00
1855	50,555	65.00	110.00	165.00
1855S	6,600	65.00	110.00	165.00
1856	26,010	65.00	110.00	165.00
1856S	34,500	65.00	110.00	165.00
1857	20,891	65.00	110.00	165.00
1857S	14,000	65.00	110.00	165.00
1858	2,133	75.00	125.00	200.00
1859	15,638	65.00	110.00	165.00
1860	7,155	65.00	110.00	165.00
1860S	7,000	65.00	120.00	185.00
1861	6,072	65.00	110.00	165.00
1862	5,785	65.00	110.00	165.00
1863	5,039	65.00	110.00	165.00
1864	2,680	85.00	150.00	200.00
1865	1,165	75.00	175.00	225.00
1866	4,030	65.00	110.00	165.00
1867	2,650	75.00	120.00	185.00
1868	4,875	65.00	110.00	165.00
1869	2,525	75.00	120.00	185.00
1870	3,535	65.00	110.00	165.00
1870S	2			Unique
1871	1,330	85.00	150.00	200.00
1872	2,030	80.00	115.00	175.00
1873 (Proofs only)	25		Proof	1250.00
1874	41,820	65.00	110.00	165.00
1875 (Proofs only)	20		Proof	———
1876 (Proofs only)	45		Proof	———
1877	1,488	100.00	225.00	325.00
1878	82,324	65.00	110.00	165.00
1879	3,030	75.00	115.00	175.00
1880	1,036	75.00	120.00	200.00
1881	554	100.00	225.00	300.00
1882	1,576	85.00	120.00	200.00
1883	989	75.00	125.00	200.00
1884	1,106	95.00	135.00	220.00
1885	910	85.00	135.00	200.00
1886	1,142	75.00	125.00	200.00
1887	6,160	65.00	110.00	165.00
1888	5,291	65.00	110.00	165.00
1889	2,429	75.00	115.00	175.00

$4.00 GOLD OR "STELLA"

Though a pattern coin, this is one of our most popular gold pieces.

This piece was first suggested by the Hon. John A. Kasson, then U.S. Minister to Austria, and it was through the efforts of Dr. W. W. Hubbell who patented the Goloid metal, used in making the Goloid Metric Dollars, that we have these beautiful and interesting pieces.

There are two distinct types of these patterns, issued only two years, known as Barber and Morgan designs. The Barber design has flowing hair and is much more common. The Morgan design has coiled hair and is excessively rare. Both very beautiful and artistic, obverse designs.

These pieces were struck in Gold, Aluminum, Copper, and White Metal. We list only those struck in Gold below.

	Quan. Minted	Proof
1879 Flowing hair	415	———
1879 Coiled hair	10	———
1880 Flowing hair	15	———
1880 Coiled hair	10	———

HALF EAGLES ($5.00 Gold Pieces)
(Coined from 1795 to 1929)

Dates prior to 1807 do not bear any mark of value. 1795 to 1798 are rare; 1799 to 1814 are fairly plentiful; and those in the 1820's are all very rare and with the possible exception of 1820, 1823 and 1826, few collectors have ever owned a half eagle of that decade. The 1822 is considered the most valuable regular issue coin of the entire United States series, there being only three specimens known and one of these is in the U.S. mint collection and therefore not available to collectors.

FINE—*Hair worn smooth but with distinct outline. After 1797 E PLURIBUS UNUM is faint but readable.*

EX. FINE—*Slight wear on hair and cheek.*

		Small Eagle	Large Eagle	
	Quan. Minted	Fine	Fine	Ex. Fine
1795 Small eagle	8,707	$625.00	$1100.00	
1795 Large eagle		800.00	1550.00	
1796	6,196	600.00	1000.00	
1797 Small eagle	3,609	750.00	1200.00	

HALF EAGLES ($5.00 Gold Pieces)

	Quan. Minted	Fine	Ex. Fine
1797 Large eagle		$650.00	$1100.00
1798 Small eagle	24,867		
1798 Large eagle		150.00	250.00

1799	7,451	200.00	325.00
1800	37,628	200.00	325.00
1802 2 over 1	53,176	200.00	325.00
1803 3 over 2	33,506	200.00	325.00
1804	30,475	200.00	325.00
1805	33,183	200.00	325.00
1806	64,093	200.00	325.00
1807 Bust facing right	32,488	200.00	325.00

FINE—LIBERTY readable but partly weak.
EX. FINE—Slight wear on high points of hair and curls.

1807 Bust facing left	51,605	200.00	325.00
1808	55,578	200.00	325.00
1809	33,875	200.00	325.00
1810	100,287	200.00	325.00
1811	99,581	200.00	325.00
1812	58,087	200.00	325.00

1813	95,428	175.00	300.00
1814 over 13	15,454	200.00	325.00
1815	635	2000.00	3000.00
1818	48,588	200.00	350.00
1819	51,723	500.00	3000.00

HALF EAGLES ($5.00 Gold Pieces)

	Quan. Minted	Fine	Ex. Fine
1820	263,806	$200.00	$350.00
1821	34,641	550.00	950.00
1822	17,796		
1823	14,485	300.00	650.00
1824	17,340	1000.00	2000.00
1825	29,060	400.00	700.00
1826	18,069	650.00	1300.00
1827	24,913	1200.00	2300.00
1828	28,029	1000.00	2000.00
1829	57,442		
1830	126,351	325.00	600.00
1831	140,594	325.00	600.00
1832	157,487	750.00	1350.00
1833	193,630	350.00	500.00
1834 Motto	50,141	375.00	650.00

	Quan. Minted	Fine	Ex. Fine
1834 No motto. Plain 4	658,028	30.00	50.00
1834 No motto. Crosslet 4		60.00	135.00
1835	371,534	30.00	50.00
1836	553,147	30.00	50.00
1837	207,121	30.00	50.00
1838	286,588	30.00	50.00
1838C	17,179	100.00	200.00
1838D	20,583	90.00	175.00

CORONET TYPE 1839-1908
Variety 1 — No motto above eagle 1839-1866

FINE—LIBERTY *readable, but partly weak. Neck hair worn, but outlines clear.*

EX. FINE—*Hair at neck sharp. Slight wear top of coronet and hair beneath.*

	Quan. Minted	Fine	Ex. Fine
1839	118,143	20.00	28.00
1839C	17,205	40.00	85.00
1839D	18,939	40.00	90.00
1840	137,382	20.00	28.00
1840C	18,992	45.00	75.00
1840D	22,896	45.00	75.00
1840O	40,120	20.00	28.00
1841	15,833	20.00	30.00
1841C	21,467	40.00	85.00
1841D	29,392	40.00	85.00
1841O (2 Known)	50		
1842	27,578	20.00	28.00

HALF EAGLES ($5.00 Gold Pieces)

	Quan. Minted	Fine	Ex. Fine
1842C	28,184	$45.00	$75.00
1842D	59,608	45.00	75.00
1842O	16,400	22.50	35.00
1843	611,205	20.00	28.00
1843C	44,201	45.00	75.00
1843D	98,452	45.00	75.00
1843O	101,075	20.00	28.00
1844	340,330	20.00	28.00
1844C	23,631	40.00	70.00
1844D	88,982	40.00	70.00
1844O	364,600	20.00	28.00
1845	417,099	20.00	28.00
1845D	90,629	40.00	65.00
1845O	41,000	40.00	65.00
1846	395,942	20.00	28.00
1846C	12,995	50.00	85.00
1846D	80,294	50.00	85.00
1846O	58,000	30.00	45.00
1847	915,981	20.00	28.00
1847C	84,151	40.00	70.00
1847D	64,405	40.00	70.00
1847O	12,000	35.00	65.00
1848	260,775	20.00	28.00
1848C	64,472	50.00	80.00
1848D	47,465	50.00	85.00
1849	133,070	20.00	28.00
1849C	64,823	50.00	80.00
1849D	39,036	50.00	80.00
1850	64,491	20.00	28.00
1850C	63,591	50.00	80.00
1850D	43,984	50.00	80.00
1851	377,505	20.00	28.00
1851C	49,176	50.00	80.00
1851D	62,710	52.50	85.00
1851O	41,000	20.00	28.00
1852	573,901	20.00	28.00
1852C	72,574	45.00	75.00
1852D	91,584	45.00	75.00
1853	305,770	20.00	28.00
1853C	65,571	50.00	80.00
1853D	89,678	50.00	80.00
1854	160,675	20.00	28.00
1854C	39,283	50.00	80.00
1854D	56,413	50.00	80.00
1854O	46,000	35.00	50.00
1854S	268	——	——
1855	117,098	20.00	28.00
1855C	39,788	45.00	75.00
1855D	22,432	50.00	80.00
1855O	11,100	50.00	80.00
1855S	61,000	30.00	50.00
1856	197,990	20.00	28.00
1856C	28,457	45.00	75.00
1856D	19,786	50.00	80.00

HALF EAGLES ($5.00 Gold Pieces)

	Quan. Minted	Fine	Ex. Fine
1856O	10,000	$65.00	$150.00
1856S	105,100	20.00	28.00
1857	98,188	20.00	28.00
1857C	31,360	45.00	75.00
1857D	17,046	50.00	80.00
1857O	13,000	40.00	65.00
1857S	87,000	25.00	40.00
1858	15,136	50.00	75.00
1858C	38,856	45.00	75.00
1858D	15,362	50.00	80.00
1858S	18,600	40.00	60.00
1859	16,814	45.00	80.00
1859C	31,847	55.00	90.00
1859D	10,366	55.00	100.00
1859S	13,220	40.00	65.00
1860	19,825	35.00	60.00
1860C	14,813	65.00	85.00
1860D	14,635	65.00	90.00
1860S	21,200	25.00	40.00
1861	688,150	20.00	28.00
1861C	6,879	125.00	275.00
1861D	1,597	575.00	1000.00
1861S	18,000	25.00	45.00
1862	4,465	65.00	125.00
1862S	9,500	50.00	90.00
1863	2,472	95.00	160.00
1863S	17,000	40.00	80.00
1864	4,220	80.00	140.00
1864S	3,888	100.00	300.00
1865	1,295	125.00	240.00
1865S	27,612	35.00	75.00
1866S No motto	9,000	55.00	75.00

Variety 2 — Motto above eagle 1866-1908

FINE—IN GOD WE TRUST worn but readable and complete.

EX. FINE—Slight wear on hair at top of head, below "L" in LIBERTY, top of coronet, and on reverse, upper wings and neck of eagle.

	Quan. Minted	Fine	Ex. Fine
1866 Motto	6,730	75.00	125.00
1866S Motto	34,920	50.00	125.00
1867	6,920	50.00	115.00
1867S	29,000	30.00	50.00
1868	5,725	50.00	100.00
1868S	52,000	35.00	50.00
1869	1,785	75.00	150.00
1869S	31,000	35.00	50.00
1870	4,035	50.00	100.00
1870CC	7,675	200.00	350.00
1870S	17,000	35.00	70.00

HALF EAGLES ($5.00 Gold Pieces)

	Quan. Minted	Fine	Ex. Fine
1871	3,230	$60.00	$150.00
1871CC	20,770	65.00	140.00
1871S	25,000	30.00	60.00
1872	1,690	125.00	250.00
1872CC	16,980	75.00	140.00
1872S	36,400	25.00	60.00
1873	112,505	20.00	28.00
1873CC	7,416	75.00	175.00
1873S	31,000	25.00	60.00
1874	3,508	65.00	180.00
1874CC	21,198	65.00	125.00
1874S	16,000	20.00	40.00
1875	220	300.00	900.00
1875CC	11,828	65.00	175.00
1875S	9,000	30.00	75.00
1876	1,477	100.00	200.00
1876CC	6,887	85.00	150.00
1876S	4,000	35.00	80.00
1877	1,152	85.00	275.00
1877CC	8,680	85.00	175.00
1877S	26,700	20.00	45.00
1878	131,740	20.00	26.00
1878CC	9,054	225.00	375.00
1878S	144,700	20.00	26.00
1879	301,950	20.00	26.00
1879CC	17,281	45.00	125.00
1879S	426,200	20.00	26.00
1880	3,166,436	20.00	26.00
1880CC	51,017	35.00	60.00
1880S	1,348,900	20.00	26.00
1881	5,708,802	20.00	26.00
1881CC	13,886	35.00	60.00
1881S	969,000	20.00	26.00
1882	2,514,568	20.00	26.00
1882CC	82,817	35.00	60.00
1882S	969,999	20.00	26.00
1883	233,461	20.00	26.00
1883CC	12,958	40.00	65.00
1883S	83,200	20.00	26.00
1884	191,078	20.00	26.00
1884CC	16,402	40.00	65.00
1884S	177,000	20.00	26.00
1885	601,506	20.00	26.00
1885S	1,211,500	20.00	26.00
1886	388,432	20.00	26.00
1886S	3,268,000	20.00	26.00
1887 (Proofs only) Beware removed mint mark	87	Proof	1200.00
1887S	1,912,000	20.00	26.00
1888	18,296	22.50	32.50
1888S	293,900	20.00	26.00
1889	7,565	75.00	125.00
1890	4,328	85.00	150.00
1890CC	53,800	25.00	35.00
1891	61,413	20.00	26.00

HALF EAGLES ($5.00 Gold Pieces)

	Quan. Minted	Fine	Ex. Fine
1891CC	208,000	$25.00	$35.00
1892	753,572	20.00	26.00
1892CC	82,968	25.00	35.00
1892O	10,000	150.00	300.00
1892S	298,400	20.00	26.00
1893	1,528,197	20.00	26.00
1893CC	60,000	25.00	35.00
1893O	110,000	25.00	35.00
1893S	224,000	20.00	26.00
1894	957,955	20.00	26.00
1894O	16,600	25.00	40.00
1894S	55,900	20.00	26.00
1895	1,345,936	20.00	26.00
1895S	112,000	20.00	26.00
1896	59,063	20.00	26.00
1896S	155,400	20.00	26.00
1897	867,883	20.00	26.00
1897S	354,000	20.00	26.00
1898	633,495	20.00	26.00
1898S	1,397,400	20.00	26.00
1899	1,710,729	20.00	26.00
1899S	1,545,000	20.00	26.00
1900	1,405,730	20.00	26.00
1900S	329,000	20.00	26.00
1901	616,040	20.00	26.00
1901S	3,648,000	20.00	26.00
1902	172,562	20.00	26.00
1902S	939,000	20.00	26.00
1903	227,024	20.00	26.00
1903S	1,855,000	20.00	26.00
1904	392,136	20.00	26.00
1904S	97,000	20.00	26.00
1905	302,308	20.00	26.00
1905S	880,700	20.00	26.00
1906	348,820	20.00	26.00
1906D	320,000	20.00	26.00
1906S	598,000	20.00	26.00
1907	626,192	20.00	26.00
1907D	888,000	20.00	26.00
1908 Liberty head	421,874	20.00	26.00

INDIAN HEAD TYPE 1908-1929

Values shown
are for pieces with
well-struck
mint marks

FINE—Knot in hair cord shows, but top feathers faint on wing.
EX. FINE—Slight wear on cheekbone and jawbone beneath. Top feathers on wing outlined but worn.

1908 Indian head	578,012	24.00	30.00
1908D	148,000	24.00	30.00

HALF EAGLES ($5.00 Gold Pieces)

	Quan. Minted	Fine	Ex. Fine
1908S	82,000	$35.00	$50.00
1909	627,138	24.00	30.00
1909D	3,423,560	24.00	30.00
1909O (Beware of altered mint mark)	34,200	87.50	120.00
1909S	297,200	24.00	30.00
1910	604,250	24.00	30.00
1910D	193,600	24.00	30.00
1910S	770,200	24.00	30.00
1911	915,139	24.00	30.00
1911D	72,500	32.50	70.00
1911S	1,416,000	24.00	30.00
1912 *Values shown*	790,144	24.00	30.00
1912S *are for pieces*	392,000	24.00	30.00
1913 *with well-struck*	916,099	24.00	30.00
1913S *mint marks*	408,000	24.00	30.00
1914	247,125	24.00	30.00
1914D	247,000	24.00	30.00
1914S	263,000	24.00	30.00
1915	588,075	24.00	30.00
1915S	164,000	24.00	30.00
1916S	240,000	24.00	30.00
1929	662,000	500.00	750.00

EAGLES ($10.00 Gold Pieces)

(Coined from 1795 to 1933; none coined between 1805 and 1837)

Although coinage extended over a long period there are really only three major types with some minor variations such as the number of stars in the first type; the liberty head was adopted in 1838 and coined until 1907, a motto being added on the reverse in 1866, the Indian head type was introduced in 1907. The rarest date Eagle is 1798.

CAPPED BUST TO RIGHT, SMALL EAGLE 1795-1797

FINE—Details on turban and head obliterated.

EX. FINE—Noticeable wear points are: hair left of eye, strand which sweeps across turban and eagle's wingtips.

		Fine	Ex. Fine
1795	5,583	600.00	925.00
1796	4,146	550.00	900.00
1797 Small eagle	2,466	550.00	900.00

EAGLES ($10.00 Gold Pieces)
CAPPED BUST TO RIGHT, HERALDIC EAGLE 1797-1804

	Quan. Minted	Fine	Ex. Fine
1797 Large eagle	12,089	$450.00	$700.00
1798 Over 97. 4 stars facing	900	675.00	1350.00
1798 Over 97. 6 stars facing	842	1400.00	3000.00
1799	37,449	275.00	400.00
1800	5,999	325.00	475.00
1801	44,344	300.00	425.00
1803	15,017	325.00	475.00
1804	3,757	400.00	675.00

CORONET TYPE 1838-1907
Variety 1 — No motto above eagle 1838-1866

FINE—*LIBERTY readable but may be slightly worn.*

EX. FINE—*Wear shows at top of head, hair below "L" in LIBERTY, top of coronet, upper part of wings and neck of eagle.*

1838	7,200	175.00	350.00
1839	38,248	125.00	275.00
1840	47,338	25.00	32.50
1841	63,131	25.00	32.50
1841O	2,500	135.00	250.00
1842	81,507	25.00	30.00
1842O	27,400	27.50	37.50
1843	75,462	25.00	30.00
1843O	175,162	25.00	30.00
1844	6,361	75.00	140.00
1844O	118,700	25.00	30.00
1845	26,153	25.00	30.00
1845O	47,500	25.00	30.00
1846	20,095	25.00	30.00
1846O	81,780	25.00	30.00
1847	862,258	25.00	30.00
1847O	571,500	25.00	30.00
1848	145,484	25.00	30.00
1848O	35,850	25.00	30.00
1849	653,618	25.00	30.00
1849O	23,900	27.50	35.00
1850	291,451	25.00	30.00

EAGLES ($10.00 Gold Pieces)

		Quan. Minted	Fine	Ex. Fine
1850O		57,500	$27.50	$37.50
1851		176,328	25.00	30.00
1851O		263,000	25.00	30.00
1852		263,106	25.00	30.00
1852O		18,000	30.00	50.00
1853		201,253	25.00	30.00
1853O		51,000	30.00	37.50
1854		54,250	25.00	30.00
1854O		52,500	30.00	40.00
1854S		123,826	25.00	37.50
1855	Values listed for all gold	121,701	25.00	30.00
1855O	coins are for choice speci-	18,000	35.00	65.00
1855S	mens. Those grading less	9,000	50.00	90.00
1856	than the conditions listed	60,490	25.00	30.00
1856O	bring proportionately less.	14,500	30.00	45.00
1856S		68,000	25.00	35.00
1857		16,606	35.00	60.00
1857O		5,500	85.00	150.00
1857S		26,000	30.00	50.00
1858	(Beware removed mint mark)	2,521	1750.00	3000.00
1858O		20,000	35.00	65.00
1858S		11,800	30.00	50.00
1859		16,093	37.50	65.00
1859O		2,300	70.00	110.00
1859S		7,000	50.00	90.00
1860		15,105	35.00	42.50
1860O		11,100	35.00	50.00
1860S		5,000	100.00	175.00
1861		113,233	25.00	35.00
1861S		15,500	27.50	37.50
1862		10,995	37.50	90.00
1862S		12,500	35.00	85.00
1863		1,248	140.00	325.00
1863S		10,000	50.00	85.00
1864		3,580	90.00	135.00
1864S		2,500	135.00	375.00
1865		4,005	75.00	125.00
1865S		16,700	85.00	300.00
1866S No motto (All Kinds)		20,000	60.00	125.00

Variety 2 — Motto above eagle 1866-1907

FINE—IN GOD WE TRUST worn but readable and complete.

EX. FINE—Wear shows at top of head, hair below "L" in LIBERTY, top of coronet, upper part of wings and neck of eagle.

1866		3,780	60.00	125.00
1866S With motto			40.00	100.00
1867		3,140	60.00	100.00
1867S		9,000	40.00	85.00

EAGLES ($10.00 Gold Pieces)

	Quan. Minted	Fine	Ex. Fine
1868	10,655	$30.00	$65.00
1868S	13,500	30.00	65.00
1869	1,855	125.00	275.00
1869S	6,430	50.00	100.00
1870	4,025	80.00	135.00
1870CC	5,908	125.00	275.00
1870S	8,000	50.00	90.00
1871	1,820	75.00	200.00
1871CC	7,185	100.00	225.00
1871S	16,500	30.00	65.00
1872	1,650	90.00	185.00
1872CC	5,500	100.00	200.00
1872S	17,300	30.00	65.00
1873	825	150.00	500.00
1873CC	4,543	110.00	250.00
1873S	12,000	30.00	80.00
1874	53,160	25.00	30.00
1874CC	16,767	50.00	90.00
1874S	10,000	35.00	80.00
1875	120	500.00	1250.00
1875CC	7,715	75.00	160.00
1876	732	135.00	300.00
1876CC	4,696	90.00	200.00
1876S	5,000	60.00	125.00
1877	817	200.00	500.00
1877CC	3,332	90.00	185.00
1877S	17,000	27.50	40.00
1878	73,800	22.50	26.00
1878CC	3,244	135.00	275.00
1878S	26,100	25.00	35.00
1879	384,770	25.00	35.00
1879CC	1,762	250.00	500.00
1879O	1,500	200.00	375.00
1879S	224,000	22.50	26.00
1880	1,644,876	22.50	26.00
1880CC	11,190	30.00	50.00
1880O	9,200	27.50	60.00
1880S	506,250	22.50	26.00
1881	3,877,260	22.50	26.00
1881CC	24,015	35.00	50.00
1881O	8,350	30.00	60.00
1881S	970,000	25.00	35.00
1882	2,324,480	25.00	35.00
1882CC	6,764	40.00	80.00
1882O	10,820	30.00	40.00
1882S	132,000	22.50	26.00
1883	208,740	22.50	26.00
1883CC	12,000	35.00	75.00
1883O	800	290.00	600.00
1883S	38,000	27.50	40.00
1884	76,905	22.50	26.00
1884CC	9,925	35.00	75.00
1884S	124,250	22.50	26.00
1885	253,527	22.50	26.00

EAGLES ($10.00 Gold Pieces)

	Quan. Minted	Fine	Ex. Fine
1885S	228,000	$22.50	$26.00
1886	236,160	22.50	26.00
1886S	826,000	22.50	26.00
1887	53,680	22.50	26.00
1887S	817,000	22.50	26.00
1888	132,996	22.50	26.00
1888O	21,335	22.50	26.00
1888S	648,700	22.50	26.00
1889	4,485	65.00	125.00
1889S	425,400	22.50	26.00
1890	58,043	22.50	26.00
1890CC	17,500	30.00	35.00
1891	91,868	22.50	26.00
1891CC	103,732	27.50	35.00
1892	797,552	22.50	26.00
1892CC	40,000	27.50	35.00
1892O	28,688	22.50	26.00
1892S	115,500	22.50	26.00
1893	1,840,895	22.50	26.00
1893CC	14,000	27.50	37.50
1893O	17,000	22.50	32.50
1893S	141,350	22.50	26.00
1894	2,470,778	22.50	26.00
1894O	107,500	27.50	35.00
1894S	25,000	27.50	37.50
1895	567,826	22.50	26.00
1895O	98,000	22.50	26.00
1895S	49,000	22.50	26.00
1896	76,348	22.50	26.00
1896S	123,750	22.50	26.00
1897	1,000,159	22.50	26.00
1897O	42,500	22.50	26.00
1897S	234,750	22.50	26.00
1898	812,197	22.50	26.00
1898S	473,600	22.50	26.00
1899	1,262,305	22.50	26.00
1899O	37,047	22.50	26.00
1899S	841,000	22.50	26.00
1900	293,960	22.50	26.00
1900S	81,000	22.50	26.00
1901	1,718,825	22.50	26.00
1901O	72,041	22.50	26.00
1901S	2,812,750	22.50	26.00
1902	82,513	22.50	26.00
1902S	469,500	22.50	26.00
1903	125,926	22.50	26.00
1903O	112,771	22.50	26.00
1903S	538,000	22.50	26.00
1904	162,038	22.50	26.00
1904O	108,950	22.50	26.00
1905	201,078	22.50	26.00
1905S	369,250	22.50	26.00
1906	165,497	22.50	26.00
1906D	981,000	22.50	26.00

EAGLES ($10.00 Gold Pieces)

	Quan. Minted	Fine	Ex. Fine
1906O	86,895	$22.50	$32.50
1906S	457,000	22.50	26.00
1907 Liberty head	1,203,973	22.50	26.00
1907D Liberty	1,030,000	22.50	26.00
1907S Liberty	210,500	22.50	26.00

INDIAN HEAD TYPE 1907-1933
Variety 1 — No motto on reverse 1907-1908

FINE—*Full LIBERTY. Feathers on bonnet noticeably worn. Eagle's left wing, leaves at left of eagle's perch and talons show wear.*

EX. FINE—*Trace of wear on cheekbone, feathers on headdress, above eagle's eye and left wing.*

	Quan. Minted	Fine	Ex. Fine
1907 Indian, "wire edge," periods before and after legends	500	250.00	400.00
1907 Rounded edge, with periods	42	1000.00	2000.00
1907 No periods	239,406	37.50	45.00
1908 No motto to left of eagle	33,500	37.50	45.00
1908D No motto	210,000	37.50	45.00

Variety 2 — Motto on reverse 1908-1933

	Quan. Minted	Fine	Ex. Fine
1908 Motto "In God We Trust" added	341,486	37.50	45.00
1908D Motto	836,500	37.50	45.00
1908S Motto	59,853	45.00	55.00
1909	184,860	37.50	45.00
1909D	121,540	37.50	45.00
1909S	292,350	37.50	45.00
1910	318,704	37.50	45.00
1910D	2,356,640	37.50	45.00
1910S	811,000	37.50	45.00
1911	505,595	37.50	45.00
1911D	30,100	45.00	60.00
1911S	51,000	45.00	60.00
1912	405,083	37.50	45.00
1912S	300,000	37.50	45.00
1913	442,071	37.50	45.00
1913S	66,000	40.00	55.00
1914	151,050	37.50	45.00
1914D	343,500	37.50	45.00
1914S	208,000	37.50	45.00
1915	351,075	37.50	45.00
1915S	59,000	45.00	70.00
1916S	138,500	37.50	45.00
1920S	126,500	1000.00	1850.00
1926	1,014,000	37.50	45.00
1930S	96,000	950.00	1600.00
1932	4,463,000	37.50	45.00
1933	312,500	1200.00	2000.00

DOUBLE EAGLES ($20.00 Gold Pieces)

(Coined for general circulation from 1850 through 1932)

This series is not collected extensively by dates except by the more wealthy collectors due to the high face value. Most of the dates are not rare except in uncirculated or proof condition; 1883 is the rarest date as only 40 were coined. Proofs before 1890 are quite rare as only 25 to 35 pieces each year were struck in that condition. The last year of coinage, 1933, was not officially released.

CORONET TYPE 1849-1907

FINE—*LIBERTY complete and readable. Last seven crown jewels show wear. Hairlines worn.*
EX. FINE—*Slight wear on curls and crown jewels. Tiny bagmarks.*

		Quan. Minted	Fine	Ex. Fine
1849 (In U. S. Mint Collection)		1		
1850		1,170,261	$50.00	$85.00
1850O		141,000	50.00	85.00
1851		2,087,155	50.00	55.00
1851O		315,000	55.00	80.00
1852		2,053,026	50.00	55.00
1852O		190,000	60.00	75.00
1853		1,261,326	50.00	55.00
1853O		71,000	65.00	95.00
1854		757,899	50.00	55.00
1854O		3,250	750.00	1400.00
1854S		141,468	55.00	75.00
1855	Values listed for all gold	364,666	50.00	55.00
1855O	coins are for choice speci-	8,000	125.00	250.00
1855S		879,675	50.00	55.00
1856	mens. Those grading less	329,878	50.00	55.00
1856O	than the conditions listed	2,250	1500.00	3000.00
1856S		1,189,750	50.00	65.00
1857	bring proportionately less.	439,375	50.00	55.00
1857O		30,000	60.00	125.00
1857S		970,500	50.00	65.00
1858		211,714	50.00	75.00
1858O		35,250	85.00	185.00
1858S		846,710	50.00	65.00
1859		43,597	60.00	100.00
1859O		9,100	125.00	275.00
1859S		636,445	50.00	65.00
1860		577,670	50.00	65.00
1860O		6,600	325.00	600.00
1860S		544,950	50.00	65.00
1861		2,976,453	50.00	55.00

DOUBLE EAGLES ($20.00 Gold Pieces)

	Quan. Minted	Fine	Ex. Fine
1861O	5,000	$150.00	$250.00
1861S	768,000	50.00	65.00
1862	92,133	60.00	125.00
1862S	854,173	50.00	65.00
1863	142,790	65.00	125.00
1863S	966,570	50.00	65.00
1864	204,285	50.00	70.00
1864S	793,660	50.00	65.00
1865	351,200	60.00	80.00
1865S	1,042,500	50.00	55.00
1866S No motto		125.00	275.00
1866 Motto	698,775	50.00	65.00
1866S Motto (all kinds)	842,250	50.00	55.00
1867	251,065	50.00	55.00
1867S	920,750	50.00	55.00
1868	98,600	50.00	70.00
1868S	837,500	50.00	55.00
1869	175,155	50.00	65.00
1869S	686,750	50.00	55.00
1870	155,185	50.00	65.00
1870CC	3,789	2250.00	4500.00
1870S	982,000	50.00	55.00
1871	80,150	60.00	70.00
1871CC	14,687	125.00	250.00
1871S	928,000	50.00	55.00
1872	251,880	50.00	55.00
1872CC	29,650	75.00	175.00
1872S	780,000	50.00	55.00
1873	1,709,825	50.00	55.00
1873CC	22,410	60.00	175.00
1873S	1,040,600	50.00	55.00
1874	366,800	50.00	55.00
1874CC	115,085	50.00	55.00
1874S	1,214,000	50.00	55.00
1875	295,740	50.00	55.00
1875CC	111,151	50.00	65.00
1875S	1,230,000	50.00	55.00
1876	583,905	50.00	55.00
1876CC	138,441	50.00	55.00
1876S	1,597,000	50.00	55.00
1877	397,670	50.00	55.00
1877CC	42,565	60.00	80.00
1877S	1,735,000	50.00	55.00
1878	543,645	50.00	55.00
1878CC	13,180	75.00	110.00
1878S	1,739,000	50.00	55.00
1879	207,630	50.00	55.00
1879CC	10,708	125.00	225.00
1879O	2,325	275.00	475.00
1879S	1,223,800	50.00	55.00
1880	51,456	50.00	55.00
1880S	836,000	50.00	55.00
1881	2,260	250.00	400.00
1881S	727,000	50.00	55.00

DOUBLE EAGLES ($20.00 Gold Pieces)

	Quan. Minted	Fine	Ex. Fine
1882	630	$250.00	$800.00
1882CC	39,140	50.00	65.00
1882S	1,125,000	50.00	55.00
1883 (Proofs only) Beware removed mint mark	40		4500.00
1883CC	59,962	60.00	80.00
1883S	1,189,000	50.00	55.00
1884 (Proofs only) Beware removed mint mark	71		3750.00
1884CC	81,139	60.00	80.00
1884S	916,000	50.00	55.00
1885	828	250.00	600.00
1885CC	9,450	100.00	200.00
1885S	683,500	50.00	55.00
1886	1,106	350.00	750.00
1887 (Proofs only) Beware removed mint mark	121		2500.00
1887S	283,000	50.00	55.00
1888	226,266	50.00	55.00
1888S	859,600	50.00	55.00
1889	44,111	50.00	65.00
1889CC	30,945	50.00	65.00
1889S	774,700	50.00	55.00
1890	75,995	50.00	55.00
1890CC	91,209	50.00	65.00
1890S	802,750	50.00	55.00
1891	1,442	125.00	275.00
1891CC	5,000	125.00	250.00
1891S	1,288,125	50.00	55.00
1892	4,523	125.00	275.00
1892CC	27,265	60.00	75.00
1892S	930,150	50.00	55.00
1893	344,339	50.00	55.00
1893CC	18,402	60.00	80.00
1893S	996,175	50.00	55.00
1894	1,368,990	50.00	55.00
1894S	1,048,550	50.00	55.00
1895	1,114,656	50.00	55.00
1895S	1,143,500	50.00	55.00
1896	792,663	50.00	55.00
1896S	1,403,925	50.00	55.00
1897	1,383,261	50.00	55.00
1897S	1,470,250	50.00	55.00
1898	170,470	50.00	55.00
1898S	2,575,175	50.00	55.00
1899	1,669,384	50.00	55.00
1899S	2,010,300	50.00	55.00
1900	1,874,584	50.00	55.00
1900S	2,459,500	50.00	55.00
1901	111,526	50.00	55.00
1901S	1,596,000	50.00	55.00
1902	31,254	50.00	55.00
1902S	1,753,625	50.00	55.00
1903	287,428	50.00	55.00
1903S	954,000	50.00	55.00
1904	6,256,797	50.00	55.00
1904S	5,134,175	50.00	55.00

DOUBLE EAGLES ($20.00 Gold Pieces)

	Quan. Minted	Fine	Ex. Fine
1905	59,011	$50.00	$55.00
1905S	1,813,000	50.00	55.00
1906	69,690	50.00	55.00
1906D	620,250	50.00	55.00
1906S	2,065,750	50.00	55.00
1907 Liberty	1,451,864	50.00	55.00
1907D Liberty	842,250	50.00	55.00
1907S Liberty	2,165,800	50.00	55.00

SAINT-GAUDENS TYPE 1907-1933

FINE—Wear evident on full length of right leg. Drapery at chest worn flat. Leaves beneath date worn. Eagle's wing tips worn noticeably.

EX. FINE—Drapery lines on chest visible. Wear on right breast, knee and below. Eagle's feathers on breast and right wing are bold.

	Quan. Minted	Fine	Ex. Fine
1907 Flying eagle, MCMVII	11,250	300.00	450.00
1907 Flying eagle, 1907	361,667	55.00	65.00
1908 No motto below eagle	4,271,551	50.00	55.00
1908D No motto	663,750	50.00	55.00
1908 Motto (In God We Trust)	156,359	50.00	55.00
1908D Motto	349,500	50.00	55.00
1908S Motto	22,000	70.00	125.00
1909 9 over 8	⎱161,282	55.00	65.00
1909 Normal date	⎰	50.00	55.00
1909D	52,500	60.00	75.00
1909S	2,774,925	50.00	55.00
1910	482,167	50.00	55.00
1910D	429,000	50.00	55.00
1910S	2,128,250	50.00	55.00
1911	197,350	50.00	55.00
1911D	846,500	50.00	55.00
1911S	775,750	50.00	55.00
1912	149,824	60.00	75.00
1913	168,838	50.00	55.00
1913D	393,500	50.00	55.00
1913S	34,000	60.00	75.00
1914	95,320	50.00	55.00
1914D	453,000	50.00	55.00
1914S	1,498,000	50.00	55.00
1915	152,050	50.00	55.00
1915S	567,500	50.00	55.00
1916S	796,000	55.00	65.00
1920	228,250	50.00	55.00
1920S	558,000	350.00	650.00

DOUBLE EAGLES ($20.00 Gold Pieces)

	Quan. Minted	Fine	Ex. Fine
1921	528,500	$800.00	$1500.00
1922	1,375,500	50.00	55.00
1922S	2,658,000	75.00	100.00
1923	566,000	50.00	55.00
1923D	1,702,250	50.00	55.00
1924	4,323,500	50.00	55.00
1924D	3,049,500	60.00	75.00
1924S	2,927,500	85.00	140.00
1925	2,831,750	50.00	55.00
1925D	2,938,500	125.00	225.00
1925S	3,776,500	65.00	100.00
1926	816,750	50.00	55.00
1926D	481,000	200.00	300.00
1926S	2,041,500	85.00	125.00
1927	2,946,750	50.00	55.00
1927D	180,000	——	——
1927S	3,107,000	200.00	300.00
1928	8,816,000	50.00	55.00
1929	1,779,750	400.00	600.00
1930S	74,000	625.00	875.00
1931	2,938,250	500.00	700.00
1931D	106,500	825.00	1150.00
1932	1,101,750	450.00	750.00
1933 (Not placed in circulation)	(445,500)		

COMMEMORATIVE COINS

The unique position occupied by Commemoratives in United States coinage is largely due to the fact that they are the only coins that have a real historical significance. No other coins bear any definite relation to historical events. It is the historical features of the Commemoratives which create interest among people who otherwise have little interest in coins.

Commemorative half dollars are considered for coinage by two committees of Congress — The Committee on Banking and Currency of the Senate, and the Committee on Coinage, Weights and Measures of the House. Congress is guided to a great extent by the reports of these committees when passing upon bills authorizing commemorative coins.

Memorial coins are issued either to commemorate special events, or to help pay for monuments or celebrations that commemorate historical persons, places or things.

A complete set of Commemorative half dollars comprises 48 types, and with the addition of mint mark varieties makes a total of 142 coins to the series.

No Commemorative coin was struck from 1940 to 1945.

COMMEMORATIVE SILVER COINS

In 1892, to commemorate the World's Columbian Exposition in Chicago, Congress authorized the coinage of a special half dollar and quarter dollar, thus starting a long line of United States commemorative coins. All commemorative coins have been distributed by private individuals or commissions; they paid the mint the face value of the coins and in turn sold the pieces at a premium to collectors. There are a few instances in which some of the very large issues were later released to circulation at face value.

COMMEMORATIVE SILVER
Isabella, Lafayette, Alabama

The commemorative coin series is collected generally in uncirculated condition and the common varieties that have been circulated are practically unsaleable. Even the rare varieties are sold at great discount when in anything but mint state.

Due to their different designs and the events they commemorate this is a popular series and is worthy of the consideration of every American collector.

Commemorative totals are given as "quantity available." In many instances a portion of the total coinage has been melted. The figures given here represent the quantity of coins that are still in the hands of collectors and dealers.

		Quan. Available	Ex. Fine	Unc.
1893	Isabella Quarter (Columbian Exposition)....	24,214	$40.00	$67.50

1900	Lafayette Dollar.........................	36,026	72.50	155.00

HALF DOLLARS
(Listed alphabetically)

1921	Alabama, "2 x 2" in field................	6,006	25.00	50.00
1921	Same, no "2 x 2"........................	59,038	17.50	35.00

COMMEMORATIVE SILVER
Albany, Antietam, Arkansas

		Quan. Available	Ex. Fine	Unc.
1936	Albany, New York	17,671	$22.50	$45.00

1937	Battle of Antietam 1862-1937	18,028	30.00	70.00

1935	Arkansas Centennial	13,012 ⎤		
1935D	Same	5,505 ⎬Set		37.50
1935S	Same	5,506 ⎦		
1936	Arkansas Centennial, same as 1935 —			
	date 1936 on reverse	9,660 ⎤		
1936D	Same	9,660 ⎬Set		37.50
1936S	Same	9,662 ⎦		
1937	Arkansas Centennial, same as 1935	5,505 ⎤		
1937D	Same	5,505 ⎬Set		40.00
1937S	Same	5,506 ⎦		
1938	Arkansas Centennial, same as 1935	3,156 ⎤		
1938D	Same	3,155 ⎬Set		60.00
1938S	Same	3,156 ⎦		
1939	Arkansas, same as 1935	2,104 ⎤		
1939D	Same	2,104 ⎬Set		225.00
1939S	Same	2,105 ⎦		
	Single type coin			12.50

COMMEMORATIVE SILVER
Bay Bridge, Boone

		Quan. Available	Ex. Fine	Unc.
1936S	San Francisco-Oakland Bay Bridge.....71,424		$10.00	$20.00

1934	Daniel Boone Bicentennial............10,007		5.00	15.00
1935	Same............................10,010 ⎫			
1935D	Same.............................5,005 ⎬ Set			40.00
1935S	Same.............................5,005 ⎭			

1935	Daniel Boone Bicentennial, same as 1934 but small 1934 added on reverse.....10,008 ⎫			
1935D	Same.............................2,003 ⎬ Set			225.00
1935S	Same.............................2,004 ⎭			
1936	D. Boone Bicentennial, same as 1934...12,012 ⎫			
1936D	Same.............................5,005 ⎬ Set			36.00
1936S	Same.............................5,006 ⎭			
1937	D. Boone Bicentennial, same as 1934....9,810 ⎫			
1937D	Same.............................2,506 ⎬ Set			125.00
1937S	Same.............................2,506 ⎭			
1938	Daniel Boone, same as 1934............2,100 ⎫			
1938D	Same.............................2,100 ⎬ Set			225.00
1938S	Same.............................2,100 ⎭			
	Single type coin..............................		5.00	13.00

COMMEMORATIVE SILVER
Bridgeport, California, Cincinnati, Cleveland

		Quan. Available	Ex. Fine	Unc.
1936	Bridgeport, Conn., Centennial............25,015		$12.00	$30.00

1925S	California Diamond Jubilee..............86,594		10.00	20.00

1936	Cincinnati Musical Center.............5,005 ⎫			
1936D	Same............................5,005 ⎬ Set			300.00
1936S	Same............................5,006 ⎭			
	Single type coin............................			100.00

1936	Cleveland, Great Lakes Exposition.........50,030		7.50	15.00

COMMEMORATIVE SILVER

Columbia, S.C., Columbian, Connecticut, Delaware

		Quan. Available	Ex. Fine	Unc.
1936	Columbia, S.C., Sesquicentennial	9,007		
1936D	Same	8,009 } Set		$100.00
1936S	Same	8,007		
	Single type coin			33.00

1892	Columbian Exposition	950,000	$2.00	4.75
1893	Same	1,550,405	1.50	3.50

1935	Connecticut Tercentenary	25,018	20.00	42.50

1936	Delaware Tercentenary	20,993	20.00	42.00

COMMEMORATIVE SILVER
Elgin, Gettysburg, Grant, Hawaiian

		Quan. Available	Ex. Fine	Unc.
1936	Elgin, Illinois, Centennial	20,015	$15.00	$32.50

| 1936 | Battle of Gettysburg 1863-1938 | 26,928 | 19.00 | 38.00 |

| 1922 | Grant Memorial, small star above word "Grant" in obv. field | 4,256 | 47.50 | 95.00 |
| 1922 | Same, no star in obverse field | 67,405 | 8.00 | 20.00 |

(Fake stars have flattened spot on reverse.)

| 1928 | Hawaiian Sesquicentennial | 10,008 | 225.00 | 410.00 |

COMMEMORATIVE SILVER
Hudson, Huguenot, Iowa, Lexington

	Quan. Available	Ex. Fine	Unc.
1935 Hudson N. Y. Sesquicentennial..............10,008		$85.00	$210.00

1924   Huguenot-Walloon Tercentenary..........142,080   10.00   21.00

1946   Iowa Centennial........................100,057   8.50   18.50

1925   Lexington-Concord Sesquicentennial.......162,013   6.50   13.00

COMMEMORATIVE SILVER
Lincoln, Long Island, Lynchburg, Maine

		Quan. Available	Ex. Fine	Unc.
1918	Illinois Centennial................100,058		$9.00	$20.00

1936	Long Island Tercentenary.............81,826	7.00	14.00

1936	Lynchburg, Va., Sesquicentennial.........20,013	15.00	32.50

1920	Maine Centennial................50,028	9.00	20.00

COMMEMORATIVE SILVER
Maryland, Missouri, Monroe, New Rochelle

		Quan. Available	Ex. Fine	Unc.
1934	Maryland Tercentenary...................	25,015	$12.00	$27.00

1921	Missouri Centennial, "2 ★ 4" above "1821"...	5,000	40.00	110.00
1921	Same, no "2 ★ 4"........................	15,428	35.00	105.00

1923S	Monroe Doctrine Centennial..............	274,077	4.00	13.00

1938	New Rochelle, N. Y. 1688-1938.............	15,266	25.00	55.00

COMMEMORATIVE SILVER
Norfolk, Oregon, Panama-Pacific

		Quan. Available	Ex. Fine	Unc.
1936	Norfolk, Va., Bicentennial	16,936	$25.00	$50.00

			Ex. Fine	Unc.
1926	Oregon Trail Memorial	47,955	5.00	15.00
1926S	Same	83,055	5.00	15.00
1928	Oregon Trail Memorial, same as 1926	6,028	5.00	16.00
1933D	Oregon Trail Memorial, same	5,008	5.00	29.00
1934D	Oregon Trail Memorial, same	7,006	5.00	15.00
1936	Oregon Trail Memorial, same as 1926	10,006	5.00	15.00
1936S	Same	5,006	6.00	20.00
1937D	Oregon Trail Mem., D mint, same as 1926	12,008	5.00	15.00
1938	Oregon Trail Mem., same as 1926	6,006 ⎫		
1938D	Same	6,005 ⎬ Set		45.00
1938S	Same	6,006 ⎭		
1939	Oregon Trail, same as 1926	3,004 ⎫		
1939D	Same	3,004 ⎬ Set		100.00
1939S	Same	3,005 ⎭		
	Single type coin		5.00	15.00

1915S	Panama Pacific Exposition, S mint	27,134	25.00	67.50

COMMEMORATIVE SILVER
Pilgrim, Rhode Island, Roanoke, Robinson

		Quan. Available	Ex. Fine	Unc.
1920	Pilgrim Tercentenary	152,112	$7.00	$15.00
1921	Same	20,053	11.00	35.00

1936	Rhode Island Tercentenary	20,013 ⎫		
1936D	Same	15,010 ⎬ Set		47.50
1936S	Same	15,011 ⎭		
	Single type coin		6.00	15.00

1937	Roanoke Island, N. C., 1587-1937	29,030	8.00	22.00

1936	Arkansas Centennial (Robinson)	25,265	8.00	20.00

COMMEMORATIVE SILVER
San Diego, Sesquicentennial, Spanish Trail, Stone Mountain

		Quan. Available	Ex. Fine	Unc.
1935S	San Diego, California-Pacific Expo.	70,132	$6.00	$14.00
1936D	Same	30,092	7.00	16.00

1926	Sesquicentennial of American Independence	141,120	5.00	14.00

1935	Old Spanish Trail 1535-1935	10,008	90.00	195.00

1925	Stone Mountain Memorial	1,314,709	4.00	10.00

COMMEMORATIVE SILVER
Texas, Vancouver, Vermont

		Quan. Available	Ex. Fine	Unc.
1934	Texas Centennial...................	61,463	$6.00	$16.00
1935	Texas Centennial, same as 1934........	9,996		
1935D	Same.............................	10,007 ⎫ Set		45.00
1935S	Same.............................	10,008 ⎭		
1936	Texas Centennial, same as 1934........	8,911 ⎫		
1936D	Same.............................	9,039 ⎬ Set		45.00
1936S	Same.............................	9,055 ⎭		
1937	Texas Centennial, same as 1934........	6,571 ⎫		
1937D	Same.............................	6,605 ⎬ Set		47.50
1937S	Same.............................	6,637 ⎭		
1938	Texas Centennial, same as 1934........	3,780 ⎫		
1938D	Same.............................	3,775 ⎬ Set		100.00
1938S	Same.............................	3,814 ⎭		
	Single type coin........................		6.00	16.00

1925S	Fort Vancouver Centennial................	14,994	35.00	75.00

1927	Vermont Sesquicentennial (Bennington)....	28,162	15.00	30.00

COMMEMORATIVE SILVER
Washington, B. T., Washington-Carver, Wisconsin

	Quan. Available	Unc.
1946 Booker T. Washington Memorial	1,000,546	
1946D	200,113	Set $ 9.00
1946S	500,279	
1947	100,017	
1947D	100,017	Set 13.00
1947S	100,017	
1948	8,005	
1948D	8,005	Set 19.00
1948S	8,005	

	Quan. Available	Unc.
1949	6,004	
1949D	6,004	Set $31.00
1949S	6,004	
1950	6,004	
1950D	6,004	Set 27.00
1950S	512,091	
1951	510,082	
1951D	7,004	Set 25.00
1951S	7,004	
Single type coin		3.00

	Quan. Available	Unc.
1951 Washington-Carver	110,018	
1951D	10,004	Set 10.00
1951S	10,004	
1952	2,006,292	
1952D	8,006	Set 14.00
1952S	8,006	

	Quan. Available	Unc.
1953	8,003	
1953D	8,003	Set 17.50
1953S	108,020	
1954	12,006	
1954D	12,006	Set 10.00
1954S	122,024	
Single type coin		2.50

	Quan. Available	Ex. Fine	Unc.
1936 Wisconsin Centennial	25,015	$13.00	$28.50

COMMEMORATIVE SILVER
York County

	Quan. Available	Ex. Fine	Unc.
1936 York County, Maine Centennial............25,015		$12.50	$23.00

COMMEMORATIVE GOLD
Grant, Lewis & Clark, Louisiana Purchase

1922 Grant Memorial Dollar, star above word "Grant"...............................5,016		115.00	205.00
1922 Same, without star 5,000		125.00	215.00

1904 Lewis and Clark Exposition Dollar..........10,025		120.00	245.00
1905 Lewis and Clark Exposition Dollar..........10,041		130.00	255.00

1903 Louisiana Purchase Jefferson Dollar.........17,500		30.00	65.00
1903 Louisiana Purchase McKinley Dollar........17,500		30.00	65.00

COMMEMORATIVE GOLD
McKinley, Panama Pacific

		Quan. Available	Ex. Fine	Unc.
1916	McKinley Memorial Dollar	9,977	$32.50	$65.00
1917	McKinley Memorial Dollar	10,000	45.00	110.00

| 1915S | Panama Pacific Exposition Dollar | 15,000 | 30.00 | 57.50 |

| 1915S | Panama Pacific Exposition $2.50 | 6,749 | 120.00 | 240.00 |

| 1915S | Panama Pacific $50 Round | 483 | | 4,500.00 |
| 1915S | Panama Pacific $50 Octagonal | 645 | | 3,750.00 |

COMMEMORATIVE GOLD
Sesquicentennial

	Quan. Available	Ex. Fine	Unc.
1926 Philadelphia Sesquicentennial $2.50.........46,019		$27.50	$52.50

CALIFORNIA FRACTIONAL GOLD PIECES

Round	Octagonal	Octagonal	Octagonal	Octagonal	Round
Quarter Dollar	Half Dollar	Dollar	Quarter Dollar	Half Dollar	Dollar

California gold quarters, halves and dollars are of two kinds:

1. Originals — Made by private companies such as assayers and jewelers in both round and octagonal form. They were made during the gold boom. The denomination spelled DOL. or DOLLAR is found on the genuine pieces. Average premium prices are:

	Ex. Fine	Unc.
Quarter Dollar, Octagonal or Round...................	$12.50	$16.50
Half Dollar, Octagonal or Round......................	13.50	20.00
Dollar, Octagonal....................................	37.00	60.00
Dollar, Round.......................................	225.00	325.00

2. Souvenir specimens do not have the words DOL. or DOLLAR and are worth considerably less than genuine specimens.

RECENT PROOF SETS
Cent — Nickel — Dime — Quarter — Half

1936..............(3,837)	$625.00		1956...........(669,384)	$ 7.00
1937..............(5,542)	200.00		1957.........(1,247,952)	4.00
1938..............(8,045)	110.00		1958...........(875,652)	8.50
1939..............(8,795)	95.00		1959.........(1,149,291)	4.50
1940.............(11,246)	80.00		1960 Large date⎰(1,691,602)	4.00
1941.............(15,287)	75.00		1960 Small date⎱	16.00
1942 With both nickels,			1961.........(3,028,244)	2.75
$90.00; one nickel..(21,120)	75.00		1962.........(3,218,019)	2.75
1950.............(51,386)	85.00		1963.........(3,075,645)	2.85
1951.............(57,500)	52.50		1964.........(3,950,762)	4.00
1952.............(81,980)	30.00		1968S.........(3,041,509)	5.50
1953............(128,800)	22.50		1969S........(2,934,631)	5.00
1954............(233,300)	10.00		1970S.........(2,632,810)	6.00
1955............(378,200)	16.00		1971S...............	5.00

Proof coins were not struck during 1943-1949 or 1965-1967.

Quantities of proof sets issued are listed in parentheses.

UNITED STATES FRACTIONAL CURRENCY

Fractional Currency is paper money issued by the United States government from 1862 to 1875 to relieve the shortage of minor coins. Specimens
are still redeemable at their face value at the Treasury Department,
Washington, D. C.

FIRST ISSUE
With facsimiles of postage stamps of the period
Perforated Edges

Denomination	V. Fine	New
5¢	$ 5.00	$17.50
10¢	5.50	17.50
25¢	7.25	21.50
50¢	10.00	25.00

Plain Edges

	V. Fine	New
5¢	1.75	3.50
10¢	1.75	3.50
25¢	2.75	6.50
50¢	5.75	10.50

SECOND ISSUE
Bust of Washington in bronze oval

	V. Fine	New
5¢	1.50	3.50
10¢	1.50	3.50
25¢	2.25	4.75
50¢	2.75	6.00

THIRD ISSUE
Green Backs

	V. Fine	New
3¢ Washington	2.25	5.25
5¢ Clark	1.75	5.25
10¢ Washington	1.15	3.25
25¢ Fessenden	2.25	5.25
50¢ Justice	4.50	8.00
50¢ Spinner	2.75	6.00

Red Backs

	V. Fine	New
5¢ Clark	4.00	10.00
10¢ Washington	2.75	8.00
25¢ Fessenden	2.75	9.00
50¢ Justice	5.00	10.50
50¢ Spinner	4.25	10.00

FOURTH ISSUE

	V. Fine	New
10¢ Liberty	1.10	2.75
15¢ Columbia	5.00	12.00
25¢ Washington	2.25	3.25
50¢ Lincoln	3.25	9.50
50¢ Stanton	2.25	4.00

FIFTH ISSUE

	V. Fine	New
10¢ Meredith	1.10	2.25
25¢ Walker	1.10	2.50
50¢ Dexter	2.25	5.50
50¢ Crawford	2.25	4.00

COLONIAL COINAGE

The first "State" or Colonial coins struck in this country were the crude "NE Shillings" by the colony of Massachusetts. These pieces were followed by the famous Massachusetts "Pine Tree Shillings" which are dated 1652; this series also included sixpence and threepence pieces of 1662. Dealers buy the more popular Colonial coins at approximately the following prices.

Fine

NE Shilling	$250.00
Massachusetts Pine Tree and Oak Tree Shillings	$50.00 to 85.00
Pine Tree Sixpence ($35.00); Pine Tree Threepence	$35.00
1787-8 Massachusetts Cents and Half Cents	$7.00
1785 to 1788 Vermont Cents	$10.00 to 115.00
1786 to 1788 New Jersey Cents	$5.00 to 20.00
1785-1788 Connecticut Cents	$4.00 to 20.00
1773 Virginia Halfpenny	$4.00 to 4.50

U. S. COIN STANDARDS

Kinds and denomina-tions of coins	Diameter	Thickness	Standard or gross weight of coins	
	Inches	Inches	Oz. Troy	Grains
SILVER:				
Dollar	1.5	.114	.859375	412.5
Half-dollar	1.205	.086	.401875	192.9
Quarter-dollar	.955	.067	.200937	96.45
Dime	.705	.053	.080375	38.58
CLAD:				
Dollar (Silver)	1.5	.114	.7906	379.5
Dollar (Cop.-Nic.)	1.5	.114	.7292	350.0
Half-dollar (Silver)	1.205	.086	.369791	177.5
Half-dollar (Cop.-Nic.)	1.205	.086	.3646	175.0
Quarter-dollar	.955	.067	.182291	87.5
Dime	.705	.053	.072812	34.95
MINOR:				
Five-cent	.835	.078	.16075	77.16
One-cent	.750	.062	.1	48.0

Kinds and denominations of coins	Weight toler-ance (above or below) on in-dividual pieces	Fineness	Fineness toler-ance on coinage ingots
	Grains	Thousandths	Thousandths
SILVER:			
Dollar	6.0	900	6
Half-dollar	4.0	900	6
Quarter-dollar	3.0	900	6
Dime	1.5	900	6
CLAD:			
Dollar (Silver)	4.0	400	6
Half-dollar (Silver)	4.0	400	6
Dollar	6.0 ⎫	75% copper, 25%	Of cladding,
Half-dollar	4.0 ⎬ nickel clad on a		not less than
Quarter-dollar	⎪ core of pure copper		30% of weight
Dime	1.5 ⎭		
MINOR:			
Five-cent	3.0	75% copper; 25% nickel	Of nickel 25
One-cent	2.0	95% copper; 5% tin & zinc	Starting 1962-95% copper; 5% zinc

INDEX

COIN FOLDERS

**A Convenient Method
of Housing Your Collection**

Made in two tones of blue . . . printed in black and silver, giving a brilliant "Jewel Case" effect to your coin collection.

Made by WHITMAN   Size Folded 5¾" x 7½"

COMPLETE LIST OF STYLES
UNITED STATES

Large Cent — 1793 to 1825
Large Cent — 1826 to 1857
Indian-Eagle Cents — 1857 to 1909
Lincoln Head Cent — 1909 to 1940
Lincoln Head Cent — Starting 1941
Lincoln Memorial Cent — Starting 1959
Cents — Plain, no printing

Half Dime — 1794 to 1873
Shield Type Nickel — 1866 to 1883
Liberty Head Nickel — 1883 to 1912
Buffalo Nickel — 1913 to 1938
Jefferson Nickel — 1938 to 1961
Jefferson Nickel — Starting 1962
Nickels — Plain, no printing

Bust Type Dime — 1796 to 1837
Liberty Seated Dime — 1837 to 1862
Liberty Seated Dime — 1863 to 1891
Barber Dime — 1892 to 1916
Mercury Head Dime — 1916 to 1945
Roosevelt Dime — Starting 1946
Dimes — Plain, no printing

Liberty Seated Quarter — 1838 to 1865
Liberty Seated Quarter — 1866 to 1891
Barber Quarter — 1892 to 1905
Barber Quarter — 1906 to 1916
Lib. Standing Quarter — 1916 to 1930
Wash. Head Quarter — 1932 to 1945
Wash. Head Quarter — 1946 to 1959
Wash. Head Quarter — Starting 1960
Quarters — Plain, no printing

Lib. Seated Half Dollar — 1839 to 1850
Lib. Seated Half Dollar — 1851 to 1862
Lib. Seated Half Dollar — 1863 to 1873
Lib. Seated Half Dollar — 1873 to 1891
Barber Half Dollar — 1892 to 1903
Barber Half Dollar — 1904 to 1915
Lib. Standing Half Dollar — 1916 to 1936
Lib. Standing Half Dollar — 1937 to 1947
Ben. Franklin Half Dollar — 1948-1963
Kennedy Half Dollar — Starting 1964
Halves — Plain, no printing

Morgan Dollar — 1878 to 1883
Morgan Dollar — 1884 to 1890
Morgan Dollar — 1891 to 1897
Morgan Dollar — 1898 to 1921
Peace Dollar — 1921 to 1935
Dollars — Plain, no printing

MISCELLANEOUS

Half Cent — 1793 to 1857
Silver Three Cent — 1851 to 1873
Two Cent — Nickel Three Cent — 1864 to 1889
Type Coins, Small Denominations
Type Coins, Large Denominations
20th Century Type Coins

ONE-A-YEAR

Cents, 1909 to Date
Nickels, 1913 to Date
Dimes, 1916 to Date
Quarters, 1916 to Date

CANADA

Large Cents — 1858 to 1920
Small Cents — Starting 1920
Silver Five Cents — 1858 to 1921
Nickels — 1922-1960
Nickels — Starting 1961
Dimes — 1858 to 1936
Dimes — Starting 1937
Quarters — 1858 to 1910
Quarters — 1911 to 1952
Quarters — Starting 1953
Halves — 1870 to 1910
Halves — 1911 to 1936
Halves — 1937-1960
Halves — Starting 1961
Silver Dollars — 1935 to 1957
Silver Dollars — Starting 1958
Quarters — Plain, no printing
Halves — Plain, no printing
Canada Coin Type Collection
Dollars — Plain, no printing